The freeway in the city

The freeway in the city

A Report to the Secretary, Department of Transportation
by
The Urban Advisors to the Federal Highway Administrator

Michael Rapuano
CHAIRMAN
LANDSCAPE ARCHITECT AND CONSULTING ENGINEER

Lawrence Halprin
LANDSCAPE ARCHITECT AND URBAN DESIGNER

Thomas C. Kavanagh
CONSULTING ENGINEER

Harry R. Powell
STRUCTURAL ENGINEER

Kevin Roche
ARCHITECT

Matthew L. Rockwell
ARCHITECT AND PLANNER

John O. Simonds
LANDSCAPE ARCHITECT AND PLANNER

Marvin R. Springer
URBAN PLANNING CONSULTANT

SECRETARY TO THE URBAN ADVISORS
Donald W. Loutzenheiser

PROJECT MANAGER
Joseph Barnett

Principles of planning and design

U.S. Government Printing Office, Washington, D.C., 1968

Library of Congress Catalog Card Number 68–60072

For sale by the Superintendent of Documents, Washington, D.C. 20402. Price $3.00

May 1, 1968

The Honorable Alan Boyd
Secretary
Department of Transportation
Washington, D. C.

Dear Mr. Secretary:

  In accordance with the instructions of Mr. Rex
Whitton, former Federal Highway Administrator, U. S.
Bureau of Public Roads, in November of 1965, creating
this group of Urban Advisors, we are transmitting in this
report our findings and recommendations with respect
to the planning and design of urban freeways.

  Respectfully submitted,

Michael Rapuano

Lawrence Halprin

Thomas Chavanagh

Harry A. Powell

Kenneth Locke

n. J. Rockwell

John O Simonds

Marvin R. Springer

Contents

Principles of urban freeway planning and design

Foreword

By Lowell K. Bridwell,

FEDERAL HIGHWAY ADMINISTRATOR

The 1960's have been years of impressive national growth. The nation has experienced unprecedented economic expansion, continuing increases in population, and accelerated urbanization of our society.

At the same time, steady growth in our national productivity and personal income has broadened our opportunities, both as individuals and as a society, to satisfy new cultural and recreational desires. Concern over what is traditionally called the "standard of living" is more and more becoming concern over the *quality* of living in America.

This new emphasis in national aspiration and public policy is having profound implications for highway transportation.

On the one hand, personal mobility remains a cherished right in a free society, and essential to the pursuit of each individual's goals. Highway transportation is the basis for the unprecedented degree of personal mobility we enjoy today, as well as for the scope and dependability of freight movement. Maintaining mobility in a growing economy clearly requires the continued growth of highway transportation.

On the other hand, highway transportation cannot be allowed to function apart from or in conflict with its environment. Inevitably, it directly affects the quality of the environment, for better or for worse. Inevitably, it interacts with other personal and community aspirations in such areas as conservation of natural beauty, provision of parks and playgrounds, preservation of historic sites, improved housing and schools and neighborhoods, cleaner air, and general community well-being. And inevitably, the potential for conflict between the highway and these other values is greatest in America's densely populated urban areas.

Simply curtailing highway improvements might eliminate such conflicts but it would not solve the problem. Such a course would produce a serious weakening of the nation's highway service capacity and, as a consequence, would impose new constraints on the movement of people and goods. In the long term, these constraints would prove a handicap to the very achievement of social goals they were meant to promote.

We must reject the kind of "either-or" approach which maintains that the nation's transportation goals are inconsistent or in contention with other personal and community aspirations. The question is not, for example, whether to preserve an historic site or to build a highway. Rather, the question is, "How do we provide needed mobility and, in the same process, contribute to other important social goals—such as the preservation of historic sites?"

It is the opportunity for social good implicit in the highway program that deserves to be emphasized. With an awareness of our social goals, and a will to serve them, the highway program can seize that opportunity.

Many aspects of this opportunity are explored in "The Freeway in the City." In this report, eight distinguished professional men have drawn upon their experience, as independent and concerned observers of the urban scene, to develop new and refreshing thinking on the principles and potentials of highway planning and design.

The authors have made a valuable contribution to our continuing effort to improve the quality of the highway transportation environment and, in doing so, to make highways serve society as fully as possible. Their report represents an important and positive development in a field of public policy characterized until recently by far too much heat and not nearly enough light. All Americans interested or involved in the future of our nation's highway system will find this document both illuminating and encouraging. It is a noteworthy step in the right direction.

Introduction

Although this report bears the Federal Highway Administration imprimatur it is actually the expression of an independent group of professionals—engineers, architects, landscape architects, and planners—who were brought together two years ago by the then Federal Highway Administrator, Rex M. Whitton, and invited to prepare a set of guidelines for the planning and design of urban expressways. The group has been further encouraged and aided by Lowell K. Bridwell, the new Federal Highway Administrator, by Frank C. Turner, Director of Public Roads, Donald W. Loutzenheiser, Secretary to the Urban Advisors, and by Joseph Barnett, Project Manager.

During the past decade particularly, state, city, and county highway departments, aided and abetted by the Bureau of Public Roads, have taken enormous strides in highway development. In scope, the network of federally aided highways has steadily expanded to a total of nearly a million miles by the end of 1967. By far the most important of the total mileage is actually the smallest in terms of linear measurement—the 41,000-mile Interstate Highway System which was begun in 1956 with a completion target of 1972. When finished, it will carry a full 20 per cent of the nation's traffic and will link more than 90 per cent of all cities having populations of 50,000 or more. Its total cost may reach $60 billion. Altogether, the Interstate System adds up to the most gigantic public works project in the history of the world.

Yet with two-thirds of it either completed or under construction, and with five years to go, the program is under heavy attack.

The Bureau and the federal government itself find it hard to understand why this multibillion-dollar aid program has aroused so much public antipathy in spite of efficient and progressive administration and superior engineering performance. So do the state highway departments, actually the dominant agents in the construction of highways. These men are justifiably proud of their role in the construction of modern America. Highways have brought about profound changes in the nation over the past 50 years—first getting farmers out of the mud, then opening up the countryside, uniting the metropolitan areas, and helping to bring an unprecedented mobility to society itself—and the men who planned and built them have by tradition worked in the public interest and, until recently, to general public acclaim. They are baffled and angered by the new and growing image of the freeway as a despoiler. They feel the critics of the freeways overlook the immense and vital services provided. They contend that the number of actual mistakes is few in view of the enormous problems involved. They point out, moreover, that the planning of urban freeways is a new science, developed for the most part since World War II, and under forced draft at that.

All this may be true, yet clearly something is wrong, and the situation cries out for new approaches, particularly in the nonengineering aspects of highway development.

The personal city

A city is made up of residential neighborhoods and office areas, of shopping strips and warehouse districts and cultural centers, of great skylines and important waterfronts—an incredibly complex interweaving of people and things, buildings and transport, living space and working space. Perhaps for this reason we often speak of it as if it were some monstrous and complicated machine. And in a sense it is, but only in one sense. Like a machine, a city has to work, certainly, and in highly elaborate ways, but if that is all it does it will never be great. People will live there in apathy and by default, wishing they had the money or the initiative to be elsewhere.

A great city, like a person, has an ambience, a personality, a soul. Anyone who doubts this should consider the case of New York City—a failure without doubt, as a machine, but as a vivid and stirring personality, something else altogether. And so it remains mecca, against impressive odds, to such diverse groups as corporations and the young.

Freeways are patently part of the machinery of a city—but perhaps at times too defiantly so. Indeed, this may be the crux of the problem, the real reason for the pickets and the violent editorials: too often the freeway program has ignored the soul of the city, at its own peril. For example, although the Bureau of Public Roads has for years urged a concern for human and cultural values in highway location, in actual practice the choice is too often made on the basis of transportation needs and cost, with emphasis on the "cost-benefit ratio," which evaluates a highway primarily from the point of view of those who drive on it. The urban highway must not only function physically, as a path for vehicular movement; it must contribute to the total city environment.

The urban core

But the means by which a highway contributes to its environment will vary as the different areas of a city vary. The old dense urban core of a large municipality like St. Louis or Philadelphia makes demands completely different from those of a residential neighborhood on its edge.

Here in the core land values are high, the structures valuable, the intricate interweaving of facilities hard to penetrate; thus the possibilities of a major linear change implicit in freeways are extremely difficult and complicated to achieve. And only part of the problem is the projection of the freeway complex itself into this dense fabric. The freeway, or arterial, with its traffic must, if it penetrates the downtown core, then face the problem of what to do with the cars once they are there. The thousands of parked vehicles themselves can destroy the very area they were meant to serve.

For this reason this report speaks of an ultimate limitation of vehicles in the core and proposes an interception of vehicles at the outskirts of the downtown where they can be stored in parking structures from which other modes of transport will bring people into and throughout the core itself.

Within the historic core, when freeways must for some compelling reason be inserted, a special set of criteria is called for. Our downtowns must be much freer than they now are of the sight and sound and fumes of cars, and of the eternal conflict between the pedestrian who is there to stroll and shop and sit in fine weather, and the mass of high-powered, swiftly moving vehicles. What we must aim toward is a new kind of traffic architecture where buildings envelop the roads—around, under, and over. Tunneling, in one form or another, is one answer, just as it was for the railroads when they penetrated downtown at the end of the 19th century. Another, on which beginnings have already been made in parts of some cities, is to separate cars from pedestrians by platform developments in which the old street pattern has been allowed to remain and the new city raised a level toward the sky where gardens and pedestrian precincts span the street and cover it. Thus the two demands, those of the driver and those of the pedestrian, are both met.

The residential area

The older residential areas of large cities surround the downtown core and are contiguous to it. Traditionally it is at the interface between these two disparate areas that some of the most difficult problems occur. Here a kind of tension is set up between residential use and financial-commercial use, and freeways have commonly been inserted between the two. In the process, however, neighborhoods have been isolated from their own commercial districts and sundered from downtown, and the freeway has served as a constricting noose around the downtown area, preventing it from expanding outward.

The problems here are different enough from those of downtown to generate their own peculiarly adaptive solutions. The residential neighborhood should be relatively quiet, uncongested, free of air pollution, and safe for children. It also requires substantial amounts of open space, for parks, playgrounds, and other recreational facilities. The freeway, this report suggests, must bring along with it as part of its multiple-use concept its own share of the amenities required in residential neighborhoods. Certainly it should be set at a different level from that of the houses and their quiet residential streets; it should be either depressed or elevated. Depressed and covered, it provides a natural opportunity for parks and playgrounds that will in addition connect the two sides of the freeway. But in either case a sufficient amount of right-of-way must be secured so that the freeway adds in sum to the open space amenities of the city.

Even here in the residential zone, buildings along the freeway can enhance the quality of the city. If the freeway is thought of as having linear redevelopment potential, then new housing can become part of the total freeway construction, and in the process integrated with the open space amenities already described.

The expanding metropolitan area

The recent broad-scale proliferation of cities into their surrounding countrysides has been made possible largely by the new network of freeways and other arterials. Here lie even greater opportunities for using the freeway as a structuring device. Once outside the densely built-up core and its contiguous residential developments, land is far less expensive and the regional freeway network can readily expand the concept of the multiple use of the corridor. Natural features—waterways, and other scenic attractions—can be bypassed and thus preserved for their proper purposes. Freeways can, in fact, create neighborhoods which will be quiet and free from noise, scenic easements can be maintained and hiking and riding trails, parks and playgrounds developed in the enclaves created by the freeway network.

The freeway network expanding into the countryside as a precursor to urbanization or as a link between urban centers differs in its demands from both the urban core and the residential area. Its effect is similar to that of the trolley car line in the early part of the 20th century, or the suburban commuter train at the end of the nineteenth. Where the freeway in the urban core must integrate with architectural imperatives, be dense and concentrated in its right of way and largely enveloped by buildings, where the residential freeway must integrate with existing housing and bring along with it the amenities required by residential developments, the new expanding interurban freeway networks become themselves the structuring devices for newer communities, linkages about which the new cities will emerge. We have as yet few new cities in America. Rather, our existing cities have tended to proliferate, filling the gaps between existing older, well-established urban centers.

New cities

But in the years ahead new cities will certainly emerge and the freeway of the future will need to be planned as an essential element in the form of the new community. We have much to learn—some of it from Europe, where a number of new cities have risen since World War II, and some of it from our own experimentation. From what we know already, however, the new cities, to be successful, will have to relinquish the ubiquitous small-scale American grid with traffic access at ground level and establish either a series of superblocks where the car penetrates only to the periphery, or multi-level developments where cars are maintained *under* the residential and commercial areas. In either case cars will be separated from housing and pedestrians horizontally or vertically.

The point is, of course, that our ideas about cities are changing. The American ideal has always been every man on his own half acre out in the countryside. But now we are beginning to wonder. We recognize the virtues of living close to work, the avoidance of long commutations, the values of diversity in experience and cultural life that urban living can provide.

Ecological goals

But these virtues mean little unless we can recapture certain amenities which make a city a decent and satisfying place to live. The most basic of these are ecological— the simple biological requirements which urban dwellers have every right to insist upon. Among these are a series of new freedoms— freedom from excessive noise, freedom from air pollution, freedom from physical danger.

In addition to such needs there are the cultural and recreational amenities which the urban center must provide—open space, views, parks, playgrounds, cultural institutions, and an environment for commercial activity which makes downtown an exciting and colorful place to be.

To fulfill all of these needs requires major change in most of our older urban centers, including their transportation systems—new freeways and also facilities for other more specialized types of transport. But it is not sufficient to say that transportation is its own reward. Angry citizen reaction is inevitable when change is imminent without a real and general improvement in the lives of those who are affected. If, however, transport facilities can assume their proper responsibility for bringing positive values other than mobility into the city, then their chance for acceptance becomes much improved.

One of the major lessons of our times is the need for responsible urban dwellers to become involved in decision-making at all levels, particularly when these decisions affect their own lives. The old, slow, craftlike participation in the actual building of the church and the street used to answer a very real need in the city dweller. Since he is now removed from the actual building process he must be given his chance through personal involvement in choices and the various options for achieving them. Groups of citizens must be involved in the complexity of the value weighing process.

In the final analysis the city is not an abstraction but a reality for the people who live in it, work in it, travel through it. Both their assumptions and their purposes will often vary. But only with their involvement can the city again become expressive of the needs and feelings of its citizens, building its symbolic image as the very embodiment of our civilization.

This is one of the reasons this report recommends a systems approach to the design of freeways. When problems were simplistic and capable of linear solutions, traditional processes sufficed. What we face now, however, are issues of great complexity, where choices are multiple and the interactions of these choices often unpredictable.

This report is directed to the Department of Transportation, the Federal Highway Administration, the Bureau of Public Roads, state, county, and municipal highway officials, and professionals in the fields of urban design and environmental planning. It is also intended as a guide for decision-makers in the federal, state, and local governments and for the broad section of the American public which has become increasingly concerned with urban highway problems. Its purpose is to present a basic statement on the urban highway—its problems and its possibilities. It presents a body of principles which highway departments and local citizens and officials can consult in evaluating alternative expressway plans. And it proposes a technique by which, the advisors believe, all critical highway design problems should be approached.

Many of the proposals which follow are not original. Some were taken from BPR publications and directives. Some were gleaned from the publications of AASHO (American Association of State Highway Officials) and the Highway Research Board. Others were taken verbatim from discussions with state and federal highway officials. But most stem from direct observation and from the interchange of ideas at sessions of the urban advisors. In the two-year study period a number of recommendations made have already been adopted and the advisors have been getting feedback. The proposals are not intended to be revolutionary but rather, taken all together, to be a creative force in the accelerated evolution of urban freeway planning and design.

Major recommendations

During its deliberations the group of urban advisors has formulated a list of principles which it feels can substantially improve urban freeways and their development process. These are specified in the body of this report. Those of highest priority for action are recapitulated in this section in the form of policy recommendations to the Federal Highway Administration for urgent consideration.

1 Expand the application of the techniques of systems analysis and operations research as the most rational approach to the problems of planning, locating, and designing urban freeways.

Expressway development, with all its social, political, economic, and physical ramifications, is so complex that it can only be effectively attacked by new or improved study procedures. As a proven method of solving similar problems, the systems approach is well established in scientific and governmental circles.

A systems group should be initiated within the federal agencies concerned, the Department of Transportation, the Department of Health, Education, and Welfare, and the Department of Housing and Urban Development, preferably acting together. This group should determine the best systems organization for all forms of urban development. It should also develop systematic techniques for rating the many values involved in urban transportation and freeway planning. As these become available they should be adopted by the operative agencies.

No planning approach, technique, or methodology, however, should be allowed to diminish the role of the intuitive designer. Improved methods of information gathering and analysis are highly desirable, but their final translation into superior design calls for creativity and professional skill which is an essential and critical step in the freeway development process.

2 Adopt the systems concept of an interdisciplinary team approach to urban freeway planning on every level—federal, state, regional, and local.

The urban freeway planning process depends for its success upon close cooperation between the professionals involved—the planner, the engineer, the landscape architect, and the architect—any one of whom may head the team. Other members should include specialists in more general fields such as sociology, economics, ecology, and political science, among others.

3 Appoint an independent review board composed of qualified professionals to serve the Federal Highway Administrator, the Director of Public Roads, the state highway engineer, or the city public works chief in an advisory capacity. This group, employing systems techniques, could offer impartial opinions and advice on controversial cases of freeway planning and location.

4 Encourage and aid formal education in urban transportation and highway planning and design. The prospect of an increasing degree of complexity in urban freeway planning demands an increasing degree of understanding, skill, and technical ability in our professionals. The federal agencies, such as the National Science Foundation and the National Council of the Arts, should subsidize experimental educational programs in our schools of environmental design, on both the undergraduate and graduate level, to motivate the student and to broaden the scientific and esthetic base.

5 Establish a system of regional urban design institutes. The logical sponsorship might be by the Department of Housing and Urban Development and the Department of Transportation, in combination. The purpose would be to provide the impetus and means for advanced research by universities, public agencies and private firms, each involving experts in all the related disciplines. Such institutes, aided by state, regional, and local levels of government, should be coordinated with other similar efforts and encouraged to set flexible goals which would best utilize regional resources and capabilities, stimulate a wholesome diversity of thinking, and eliminate rigid standardization.

   The institutes might also organize regional interdisciplinary review boards to appraise and recommend, in an advisory capacity, on all regional highway proposals.

6 Encourage the formulation within each state of a total environmental planning commission. Such a body, representing the legislature, the governor, and the most important state agencies, should be charged with the responsibility for cordinating all physical planning within the state. All state, regional, and local proposals relating to the use of land and affecting the quality of the landscape environment would be reviewed. Freeway and other transportation proposals would be specifically included.

7 Coordinate freeway considerations with the comprehensive planning of every affected community, city, and region. It is not enough to espouse this principle in theory. The planning and design of a freeway in the urban environment should be, in fact, accomplished by a competent planning body concerned with the shaping of each community, region, and state and its highways into a balanced and integrated system. Proper weight should be given to the convenience, safety, comfort, beauty, and economic viability of every area served.

Highway planning and design must be considered a joint venture between city, county, and state governments in cooperation with strong regional planning agencies. Throughout the planning process, information on proposals should be made available to government agencies and to civic and other organizations in the interest of developing public understanding and support. It has been well said that every freeway is a political statement.

8 Promote the integration of freeways with all other elements of the urban transportation system. These include not only such facilities as arterial streets and vehicular parking areas, but also other transit systems, trains, subways, etc., even patterns of pedestrian movement. The planning and development of such a coordinated system for a metropolitan region should accompany that of the freeway.

9 Stimulate more research on better ways of moving people and goods. The nation and its highway planners look to the Department of Transportation for a masterful study aimed at the coordination of all forms of transport by land, air, and water. The planning of urban freeways should be carried forward in this larger context.

10 Investigate the possibilities of giving highway departments the authority to condemn and purchase lands adjacent to a proposed freeway or interchange. The states could then sell or lease the excess property as "improved land," for the presence of the highway would greatly enhance its access, exposure, and value for many private or public development projects. The income benefits would help to defray, or perhaps would even cover, the costs of all new highway development. The relief to taxpayers would be enormous.

Such land taking and land use should, of course, be in keeping with community objectives and official plans. The usurping of developed areas for expanded highway purposes is not intended.

State and federal legislation are necessary.

Legal means and planning techniques should also be developed by which long-range and multipurpose transportation rights-of-way may be delineated and acquired. Such advance planning would have many salutary effects. It would eliminate the costly disruption of short-term highway planning, provide for coordinated systems of transportation routing, and create a framework of movement and access, around which the metropolitan areas could be logically structured.

11 Provide a more equitable basis of compensation for lands acquired for highway purposes. In urban areas especially, many displaced families and businesses, unable to locate or afford comparable living or commercial space, are subjected to severe hardship. It is natural that they fight back, and they have been fighting back.

The price of properties condemned or purchased through negotiation should reflect the true and reasonable replacement values and moving costs rather than the present criterion of "fair market value." This would at one stroke eliminate a major source of hardship and contention.

To reduce further the disruption caused by highway land acquisition, provision should be made, as a part of every highway planning study, for an orderly program of relocation of existing residents and businesses. Such programs should be developed concurrently with the preparation of preliminary plans for corridor approval.

12 Stimulate increased emphasis on the exploration and use of new modes of urban transit. New types of vehicles, transitways, and terminals are envisioned, as well as new sources of energy.

Improvements to existing forms of transit, and bus transit particularly, would also insure better utilization of existing street capacity and (for comparable numbers of persons transported) effect a drastic reduction in vehicular traffic. Possibilities include express busses from depot to depot, streets designated for bus movement exclusively, and new transit plazas and transfer points designed for a high level of comfort and convenience.

13 Encourage the multiple utilization of urban freeway rights-of-way. Urban freeway corridors must be more efficiently used to provide urgently needed space for such other purposes as housing, commerce, industry, and recreation. This concept envisions the highway as but one occupant of the right-of-way land and the space above or below it. Its planning, if related to urban renewal, can help restructure the city in a more efficient and orderly way. The use of the space beside, below, or above the freeway should be planned and designed at the same time as the freeway itself.

It is urged that the Department of Housing and Urban Development ment join with the Department of Transportation in the initiation of a series of major projects demonstrating the possibilities of the imaginative multiple use of freeway corridors. Such projects could become an instrument for developing new procedures, financial aid programs, and enabling legislation.

14 Encourage state highway departments and local agencies to purchase and develop freeway-recreation corridors jointly. Freeways should not only provide access to, but should be considered in themselves as major recreation facilities. A bold approach is envisoned by which the freeway is designed to move through an expanded right-of-way purchased by the highway department in concert with municipalities, and devoted to scenic and recreation purposes. Such a multiple use corridor would provide, besides the roadway, such pleasures as fishing and boating lakes and streams, golf courses, game courts, riding trails, wildlife sanctuaries and conservation lands.

These freeway-recreation corridors could connect with, and bring into the urban metropolitan areas, suburban or rural attributes.

15 Develop and promote the passage by states and the federal government of advanced highway-related enabling legislation. Present highways are to a large extent the three-dimensional representation of existing laws. If more creative highway planning and design concepts are to be realized, they must be preceded by legislation to permit and encourage them. Model legislation and guidance should be provided by the Bureau of Public Roads and the Department of Transportation, based upon a comprehensive analysis of current laws, needs, and possibilities.

16 Encourage a high level of visual quality in every proposed freeway. Each highway plan reviewed should demonstrate careful consideration of esthetic values, a systematic approach by which such are to be achieved, and evidence that the highway in fact provides a continuing sequence of rewarding visual experiences. Urban freeways should contribute to the beauty of the regions through which they pass, from the standpoint of both the users and viewers of the facility. The highway beautification program of the Bureau of Public Roads is a very good beginning.

Principles of urban freeway planning and design

It is recognized that the application to any one highway project of all principles here listed would be impossible; many would be inappropriate, and some unfeasible. It is proposed, rather, that these principles, taken together, be used as a general checklist to improve the performance, appearance, and acceptance of urban freeways.

1

Comprehensive planning and community values

"The essence of planning is not merely
the catching up with reality . . .
its chief value lies in anticipating and
guiding future events."   IRA J. BACH

If there is any one concept which is foremost in the consideration of urban freeways, it is that of "comprehensive planning." Without far-sighted cooperation between highway and city agencies we are all too certain to end up with a costly, chaotic, disorganized urban mess. For the same explosive postwar growth which stimulated the Interstate program also created crushing metropolitan troubles which the construction of new highways can only aggravate unless the roads are planned as a specific remedial measure. Indeed, even without these new urban difficulties, not many cities by the mid-1950's were able to accommodate new freeways without sacrificing part of a park, access to a river, the view of a proud landmark, or the integrity of a neighborhood, unless the freeways were conceived specifically to recognize such factors. Many were not.

The city plan today consists of not one map, but many. It is, in fact, an agglomeration of plans, reports, and diagrams that together record the structure and pulse of the city and chart its future course. Increasingly it embodies all policies of the local government—economic, social, and political.

To understand the physical nature of a metropolitan region one must understand all those factors which influence its evolving structure. The values of the community are among the most important of these.

Others, more specifically physical, include:

TERRAIN FEATURES. Rivers, lakes, hills, mountains, oceans, swamps, and similar physiographic features are significant determinants of the physical form of urban areas.

TRANSPORTATION FACILITIES. The availability of transportation, or the possibility of its becoming available, has often been the determining factor in a city's location. Water transport and railroads were the early major determinants in the location and physical form of American cities. Electric trolley lines and mass rail transit systems created distinct densities and forms for the cities which were influenced by these types of transportation. In recent years all other modes of transportation have been replaced by the airport and the highway as the molders of urban form. Of the two more recent influencing transportation types, the highway has had by far the greatest impact and will continue to be a major structuring element of our urban areas.

OPEN SPACE. The land set aside as permanent open space ranks with highways as a major structuring element of an urban area. The open space may be in the form of parks, forest preserves, institutional grounds, water areas, or even agricultural or flood plain areas, though the agricultural area in proximity to a growing urban center is usually not permanent. The open space pattern tends to divide the urban area into identifiable units, delineates boundaries, gives the urban complex of buildings, streets, and utilities a setting and a human scale, and furnishes focal points around which neighborhoods and often whole communities are organized. Freeways, particularly those with parkway features, can contribute to the open space of the city.

UTILITY SYSTEMS. The availability or lack of urban utility services, such as water supply, sanitary sewerage, and gas, influences urban form and often is a factor determining what areas will develop and when. The cost of providing utility services, such as sanitary sewers, can certainly be a deterrent to urban development in the particular area. Generally, the economic cost of urban utilities and not the physical ability to provide them is the influencing factor encouraging or discouraging the direction of urban expansion.

REGULATION OF LAND USE. In this country we have only limited examples of predetermined land use patterns implemented by regulations, such as zoning, which have influenced the urban form. The confusion caused by new localities, each having its own controls, and without proper inter-relationship, has curtailed the effectiveness of land use regulations for the broader metropolitan regions. Such regulations do exist in many European countries, as in the

Netherlands, England, and some Scandinavian countries, and in these countries they have been effective in directing the pattern of urban form. The problems of local application of land use regulations in an urban complex made up of many local units of government have thus far curtailed the effectiveness of land use regulations in this country.

EXISTING LAND USE INFLUENCE. The location of various types of land use in urban areas has influenced the form and direction of future urbanization in many areas. Often cement, petrochemical, or similar heavy industrial plants have adversely influenced the surrounding area for residential use while the convenience of a shopping center, office center, or institution may encourage urban expansion in a certain direction. Generally, the influence of existing land uses on the urban form is local in nature and not a major structuring factor in the urban region.

JURISDICTIONAL CLIMATE. Nearly all of the larger urban areas are composed of a complex of governmental units whose boundaries, responsibilities, and aspirations are varied. The conditions in one municipality or district may be conducive to rapid development, while those in another could have a retarding influence. The quality and policies of a school system in one part of an urban area, for example, may stimulate or deter development. The patchwork arrangement of local government jurisdictions creates developmental frictions and complicates the planning and regulation of development along logical lines.

ENTREPRENEURIAL DECISIONS. The developer, investor, realtor, or landowner can, through enterprise, influence of public opinion, and promotion, stimulate the development of land and thus alter the form of an urban area, usually aided by one or more of the other structuring elements such as utilities, land use, terrain, or transportation facilities.

Of all the strictly physical elements influencing the physical environment of our urban areas, one stands out as having the greatest impact and potential: namely, transportation facilities. Of these, the highway is the most significant, most controversial, and most promising.

It is unfortunate, therefore, that planners have in the past so often failed to give the highway engineers information specific enough for their work. The result has been an unhappy cleavage between planners, and state and city highway departments, some of which have tended to become "antiplanning."

More recently, both planners and engineers have taken measures to bridge the gap. Since the passage of the Defense Highway Act of 1941, the comprehensive Urban Federal-Aid program in 1944, and more particularly since the passage of the 1962 Federal Highway Act, it can be said that highway planners have made an effort to cooperate and work with the city planners in locating and designing new freeways in a manner compatible with the city's proposed development or redevelopment.

The day is at hand when transportation planning will take its proper place, simply because it must, in the comprehensive planning program of every city. Nowhere can this process be better employed, cooperatively, than in the design of the urban highway with its considerable effect on the environment and the institutions of men.

The force of the freeway and the total transportation transit system as form-givers may be clearly seen in a study recently prepared by the Northeastern Illinois Planning Commission. Exploring alternative diagrams for regional development, the study presents three entirely different possibilities, each demonstrating how important a key to ultimate land use is the choice of transportation methods, as well as routes.

In the FINGER plan concept of regional development, a main mover would be mass transit. The probable result would be growth in narrow bands or corridors along commuter transit routes. Expressways would move circumferentially and radially between the fingers.

The CLUSTER concept promotes the growth of balanced "new town" clusters. Their populations would range from 10,000 to 100,000 persons and each cluster would be served by an interconnected system of expressways and major highways aligned between clusters; providing easy multi-directional travel in all parts of the region. Supplementary mass transit systems would generally connect cluster centers with each other and with the center city.

The SATELLITE plan of development envisions major self-sufficient satellite cities of 500,000 to 1,000,000 population. Each would embrace its own commercial and cultural center or centers and would be defined and surrounded by extensive green belts of agricultural, flood plain, or other open space land. Expressways would loop between and interconnect satellites and the regional core. Rapid transit would link all centers to each other and to the core.

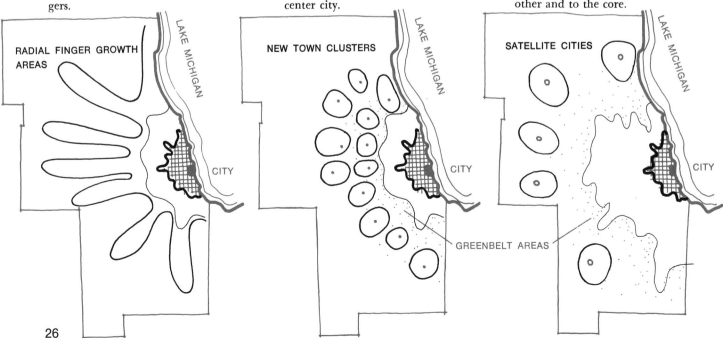

RADIAL FINGER GROWTH AREAS

LAKE MICHIGAN

CITY

NEW TOWN CLUSTERS

LAKE MICHIGAN

CITY

GREENBELT AREAS

SATELLITE CITIES

LAKE MICHIGAN

CITY

1/1

Overall development goals for the entire urban area must be set which can serve as a background for highway and all other physical planning. The highway system and all of the other physical elements of an urban area can only be effectively planned and built when an overall concept exists as to the development objectives of the area. Lack of such clearly established objectives is the cause of much of the conflict, confusion, and lack of coordination experienced in cities today. Without a concept of how the parts of the community should be assembled and work together, it is unlikely that the highway system, no matter how well engineered, will satisfactorily serve its several purposes in the region.

1/2

Local governments should insure maximum benefits to the local area by exercising their primary responsibility for community planning. Each should prepare and keep current a comprehensive plan for the physical development of the community. In its preparation competent planning services should be engaged on a continuing basis and the state highway department should be consulted frequently.

1/3

Communities, particularly in metropolitan areas, should participate in regional planning activities. Workable associations or commissions should be formed through which continuing and coordinated planning can be carried out in cooperation with state and federal agencies on a regional basis. Only on a regional basis can most transportation and transit planning problems be solved effectively.

1/4

Local governments and regional associations should work to maximize the efficiency and effectiveness of interarea freeways and arterials. They should integrate traffic planning, management, and controls on an areawide basis. Regional efforts should be supplemented with local land use controls, street widening, and other supporting measures.

1/5

The highway system should be planned and developed as a joint venture between city, county, and state officials. The elected officials of a community have an important part to play in highway planning and design. The state highway departments should cooperate with them in the acquisition, development, administration, and maintenance of highway-related lands. Perhaps no other area of highway development holds as much promise as a program of joint highway department-local government action. New attitudes, new personnel, new legislature will be needed.

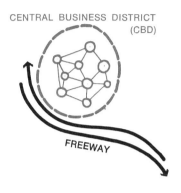

Compact vital CBD

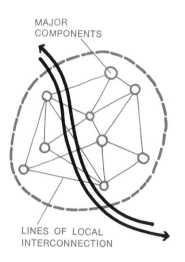

CBD weakened — split and dispersed

Within a theoretical central business district (CBD) above, the red circles represent major components such as banks, department stores, civic centers, regional sports facilities, or entertainment districts. The red lines represent lines of local vehicular or pedestrian circulation. A closely knit set of CBD components is mutually sustaining. A compact center makes for easy connections in terms of time, distance, and friction. Dispersion of CBD components also disperses the advantages of "downtown".

1/6

The size, character, and form of a city is greatly influenced by its tranportation diagram. Cities with transportation systems geared to high-speed automobile travel tend to grow extensively, with emphasis on low to medium-density housing, spread of suburban communities, and decentralization of shopping, cultural activities, business and industry. Cities discouraging automobile traffic but providing efficient rapid transit are likely to be more closely concentrated, with high-density residential areas, and a more active central core.

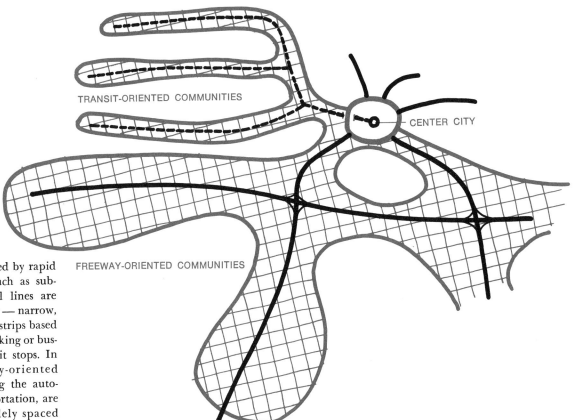

TRANSIT-ORIENTED COMMUNITIES

CENTER CITY

FREEWAY-ORIENTED COMMUNITIES

Communities shaped by rapid transit facilities such as subways or other rail lines are likely to be linear — narrow, densely populated strips based on shortness of walking or bussing time to transit stops. In contrast, freeway-oriented communities, using the automobile for transportation, are usually more widely spaced and open. The two opposing community types should be inter-related only with great care.

1/7

Urban highways must be integrated with urban design. There must be concern for the esthetic, as well as the functional planning, of city areas. Professionals trained in this point of view should be involved in the design of all freeways.

1/8

Successful freeway planning must employ the most advanced problem solving techniques. Highway planning and design must exploit new methods by which the best minds in the related disciplines can be brought to bear upon the planning process. Such a method, systems analysis, is described in chapter 7.

Urban freeway location and design should be determined by expert judgment as well as by rational response to all quantifiable factors. All pertinent factors which can be reduced to quantitative values should be charted, graphed, or otherwise applied as input. But certain factors, no less valid, such as visual elements or social implications, are more difficult to quantify and can only be evaluated through consultations with recognized authorities in each field. Intuitive judgments may in some cases be a deciding factor. They should in all cases be weighed.

In the absence of an effective comprehensive planning authority, the state highway department should assume the responsibility for assembling the wide variety of talents and coordinating the necessary studies required to make the highway a logical, sensible, and integral part of the city environment.

There is an absorptive capacity of a city for cars, just as there is of a building for occupants. This is determined by the capacity of all the streets together. When it is exceeded, health and safety as well as environmental quality are jeopardized, and the number of cars must be limited.

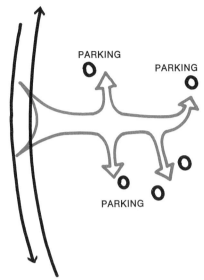

Traffic ejected into the urban area from an interchange must be absorbed by the area. If the absorptive capacity (parking facilities and street lanes) is not present, it should be planned for local development at the same time as the interchange.

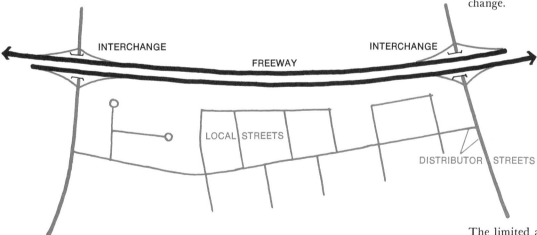

Highway planning must regard the entire rubber-tired transportation system, from freeways and major thoroughfares to local streets to storage and transfer facilities, as part of a single vehicular system interconnecting the region. All vehicular trips whether on a freeway or not, start and end in a storage or transfer facility, and almost all of them also pass through a variety of local streets. Coordination with these is essential if the freeway is to operate efficiently.

The limited access concept of freeway development should be extended where feasible to all through or distributor roads within the metropolitan region. While building frontage would not be permitted on these thoroughfares, connections to local streets would be encouraged and facilitated.

For instance a system of radial freeways should not be focused on the center of a city without the provision of circumferential or cross-region routes. This can only result in unmanageable traffic congestion near the core. A combination of radial and circumferential routes, or a modified quadrangular system of freeways spaced to serve the entire region as well as to provide access to the heart of the city and interconnect major regional traffic generators, is generally required. The spacing of freeways at about 3-mile intervals in urban areas, with interspersed and interconnecting major thoroughfares in the intervening areas, usually provides good service and permits the freeways to be designed on a more modest scale than those more widely spaced. Freeways 10 or 12 or 16 lanes wide are grim destroyers of the city, the landscape, and the motorist himself. They are inflexible and inhuman. They are dangerous.

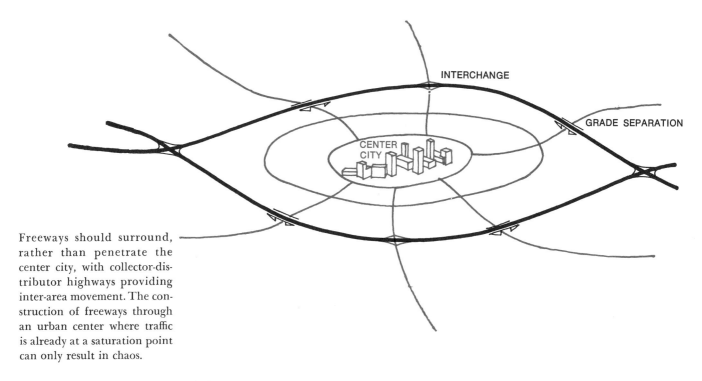

Freeways should surround, rather than penetrate the center city, with collector-distributor highways providing inter-area movement. The construction of freeways through an urban center where traffic is already at a saturation point can only result in chaos.

1/12

A concentration of large volumes of regionally oriented traffic in or near the center of a city is contrary to the best interest of both the central city and the highway user. From one-half to two-thirds of the traffic in the average central city need not be there, since it has neither origin nor destination in the central core, and would instead gladly take a bypass if there were one. Such bypasses should be developed for major through movements. In addition, truck arterials approaching the city should move into separate corridors so that large intercity trucks need *not* enter city centers, but can proceed instead to terminals from which the goods can be otherwise dispersed.

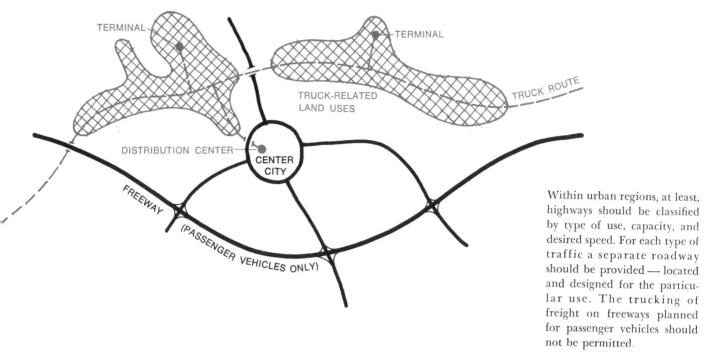

TERMINAL

TERMINAL

TRUCK-RELATED
LAND USES

TRUCK ROUTE

DISTRIBUTION CENTER

CENTER
CITY

FREEWAY

(PASSENGER VEHICLES ONLY)

Within urban regions, at least, highways should be classified by type of use, capacity, and desired speed. For each type of traffic a separate roadway should be provided — located and designed for the particular use. The trucking of freight on freeways planned for passenger vehicles should not be permitted.

1/13

The urban highway system must be specially geared to the needs of important traffic generators. While the highways must feed and drain all contiguous areas, it is of critical importance that they provide direct connection to such major activity centers as central business districts, industrial areas, port facilities, stadiums, airports, and regional commercial centers. Access to centers of employment is a related and equally vital function, and all highway planning must involve a careful consideration of changing employment patterns.

1/14

Advance planning and right-of-way acquisition is in the public interest and should be emphasized. Great savings in acquisition costs are effected and other benefits accrue when highway acquisition precedes and stimulates, rather than disrupts, land development. Rights-of-way for expressways should be acquired while areas are still vacant, are being subdivided, or redeveloped for more intensive use. Acquisition leadtime should be extended. Such advance right-of-way acquisition can be coordinated with the acquisition of land for other public needs such as schools and parks.

1/15

Highway design should be differentiated to fit the projected land use pattern. Where highways can be planned and constructed in advance of adjacent urban development, they can have a major influence on the future urban form. This influence should be considered along with other elements of the highway design. A highway designed to stimulate residential development will differ from one aimed at producing commercial or industrial areas. Adaptation of highway design details, such as the provision of frontage roads, use of depressed and elevated sections, adjustment to terrain, and the location and spacing of interchanges and grade separations, makes it possible to reinforce the land-use plan and guide the urban pattern. Such guiding or structuring influence should extend throughout the potential area of urbanization of the region.

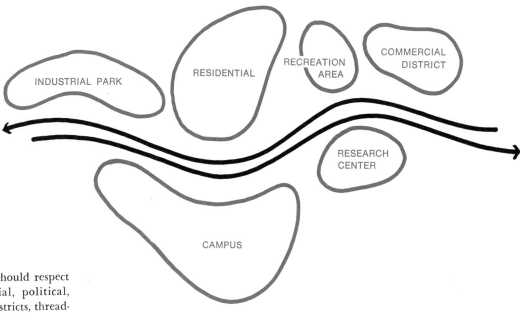

An expressway should respect established social, political, and economic districts, threading between them.

1/16

Freeways in urban areas should be located to interconnect, not split, the various land-use areas as they exist and as they are planned for the future. Many forms of land use require for their proper function areas of certain size and conformation, together with supporting facilities, and these should not be disrupted by major traffic ways. A residential neighborhood with its elementary school, parks, shopping and churches on local streets in a quiet environment is only one example. Similar units exist for industrial complexes, business districts, medical centers, and so on. Where a highway unavoidably enters an integral land use unit, disruption is minimized by the use of such devices as short tunnels, crossovers, and even construction over the freeway.

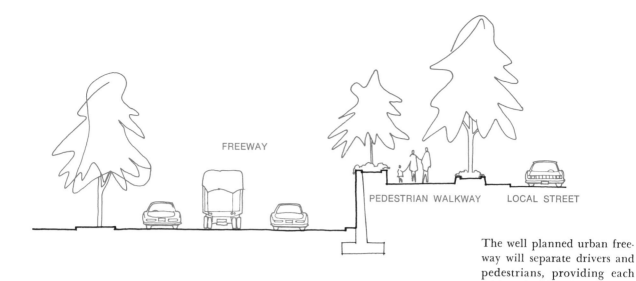

FREEWAY

PEDESTRIAN WALKWAY   LOCAL STREET

The well planned urban freeway will separate drivers and
pedestrians, providing each
with suitable channels for
movement.

1/17

Where appropriate the urban freeway can provide a logical and useful boundary
between different land use areas. Such a separation is welcome, for example, between a heavy industrial complex and a recreation area, or between a residential
neighborhood and a regional shopping center with its attendant traffic and extensive parking areas.

1/18

Sufficient cross-freeway vehicular and pedestrian connections must be provided and
strategically located. Overpasses or underpasses should maintain adequate communication between one side and the other. Cross street communication is maximum where a tunnel or continuous overhead structure is provided, and can be
facilitated by narrowing the highway in the section to be crossed.

The crossings, as important connecting elements for the adjacent land, should
be coordinated with comprehensive land use and local thoroughfare plans.

1/19

An urban highway should be so located and designed as to enhance rather than
destroy a city's best attributes. Such attributes include:
A safe, clean, and healthful living environment
Unified neighborhoods, communities, shopping districts, institutional centers, in-
    dustrial districts, and recreation areas
A dynamic and cohesive central core or cores
Inter-related systems of vehicular and pedestrian movement
A system of parks and open spaces
Historic areas and landmarks
Topographic superlatives
A composite of all those cultural and environmental components and qualities
    which together yield a satisfying way of life

1/20

Expressways should blend into the community. This is especially true in regard
to their effect upon the established street pattern, natural topographic features,
landmarks, prominent buildings, parks, and other physical elements which to-

296-930 O - 68 - 3

gether produce its character. Expressways should flow around activity centers. They must relate visually by form, scale, and all other design characteristics.

Urban highway planning must recognize and differentiate between that which is a permanent structuring feature of the community and that on which there is some area of community agreement that change be made. It is important that the unique and dominant form-giving elements of a city or region be preserved without disruption.

1/21

Freeways should not encroach upon park land, playgrounds, squares, plazas, or other open space preserves. They should add to rather than subtract from the city's open spaces. A careful study of impact upon park and recreational resources should be an essential part of every freeway location proposal. If as a last recourse, all other alternatives having been exhausted, it is agreed by highway and local officials that the freeway must usurp such areas, then replacement land and facilities of equal open space value to the affected community should be provided with highway funds prior to, or concurrently with, the freeway construction.

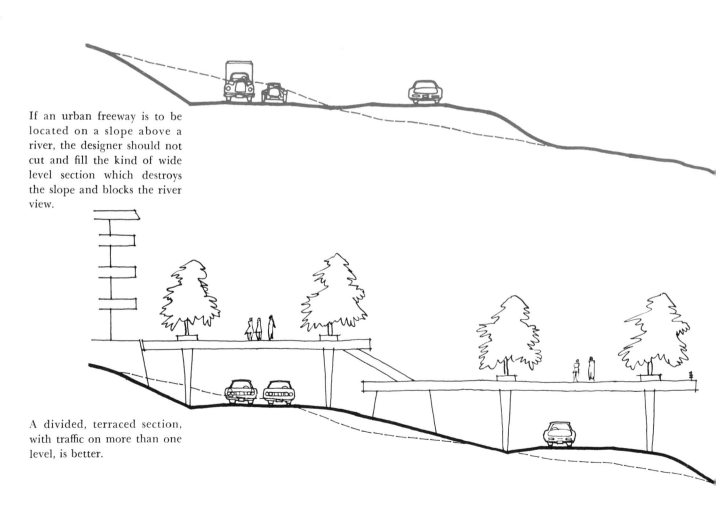

If an urban freeway is to be located on a slope above a river, the designer should not cut and fill the kind of wide level section which destroys the slope and blocks the river view.

A divided, terraced section, with traffic on more than one level, is better.

1/22

Highway location and design must consider the viewpoint of area residents. The impact of the freeway on residents in the adjacent areas should be taken into account. Land takings should not mutilate or isolate remaining properties. Roadway sections, structures, and furnishings such as lighting and signage should be so designed as to foster "good neighbor" relations. When the responsible viewpoint of local residents is in opposition to freeway proposals, the local point of view should be given high weighting, and all other possibilities explored.

1/23

Sufficient testimony on freeway planning and design proposals should be heard by concerned public officials at all levels to give them a clear picture of the facts, alternatives, and consequences, before their decisions are rendered.

1/24

If sufficient right-of-way width is purchased, the negative effects on adjacent properties remaining are reduced or eliminated. In the process, however, neighborhoods should not be wiped out.

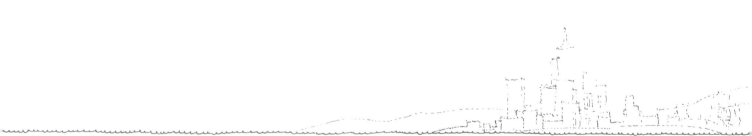

At best a city park can share the right-of-way, the river, and the view.

2

The view
from
the freeway

"Travel is not solely for the purpose of
arriving—there should be
pleasure along the way, and a window
on the world."
THE NEW YORKER

The visual enjoyment of a highway is sometimes an experience beyond
analysis. To sweep along a freeway and into a city at dusk, as the sunset
fades against the buildings and shadows deepen while myriad lights flick
on among the darkening cubes, is to see the urban landscape in a new
and magical way. Similarly, an early morning haze on the harbor can
produce a deep and lasting emotional impression of a city.

But such experiences are as a rule coincidental. Indeed, often the
grandest views from our highways have been produced so unconsciously
that they are marred by guardrails or by concrete parapets that reach
above eye level.

Views seen from and of our urban freeways must be deliberately
planned, as evolving sequences of visual impressions which reveal the
rich complexity of the city. This can only be achieved by making far better
use, in the highway planning and design process, of those professionals
who have been trained in visual structuring and in landscape development.

Beauty on an urban freeway has many aspects. There are the views
seen by the driver and his passengers; there is the freeway as a flowing
element in the three-dimensional structure of the total city; there is the
roadway itself, with its bridges and signs, colors and lights and textures;
and there are the shapes of the land it is built upon, including the trees
and other plant growth.

The essential beauty of an urban freeway lies in the sweeping forms
of the highway itself, in the unique forms of the city, and in their inter-
relationship. It is basic that highway "decoration" in any form is super-

ficial and distracting. For beauty in the highway—as in any place, or space, or object, is inherent. It is a quality perceived by the user or viewer when, and only when, everything is working well together.

2/1

Every urban expressway should be an esthetic statement. All policies or regulations relating to highway development must provide that flexibility and freedom of choice essential to creative design.

2/2

Beauty in freeway design is a result of the sum total of carefully planned and sensitively handled elements. Full consideration must be given to location, alignment, cross section, scale, environmental impact, architectural detailing, and landscape development. The beauty of a highway is often enhanced by utmost simplicity in the design of the roadway and bridges, and in such appurtenances as guardrails, signs, and lighting standards.

2/3

By location and design, urban thoroughfares should be pleasant to drive. Contributing factors include an ease in finding direction, apparent directness of routing toward desired destinations, and a sense of smooth uninterrupted flow, in harmony with the landscape forms and well related to architectural features.

2/4

The urban highway should provide a variety of visual experiences. Views of similar features from similar distances and elevations and with similar enframement or lack of enframement are bound to be monotonous.

Visual interest and scenic richness are achieved by providing a variety of subjects seen from a variety of viewing situations with each view or vista considered as one element of a studied and interrelated visual experience. It is the conscious playing of the near against the far, the light against the dark, the natural against the architectural, that has produced our most handsome scenic highways.

When roads reach rivers, they should not simply ride the shorelines for long distances, but should extract the full dramatic potential. To run parallel to an edge or shoreline for long distances produces monotony.

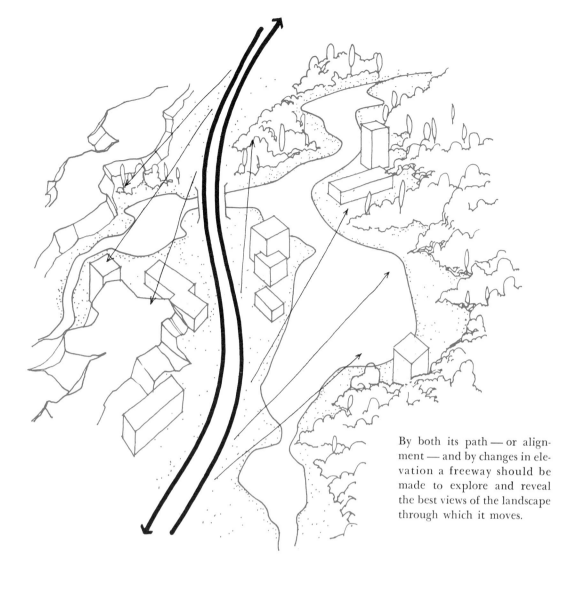

By both its path — or alignment — and by changes in elevation a freeway should be made to explore and reveal the best views of the landscape through which it moves.

NORMAL RIGHT-OF-WAY

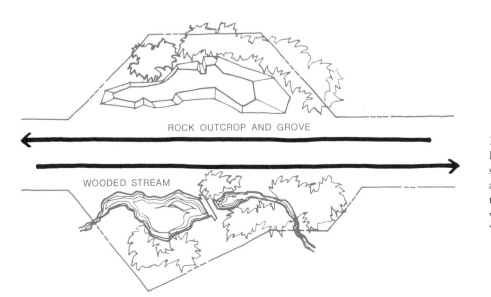

ROCK OUTCROP AND GROVE

WOODED STREAM

Even within urban areas the legally prescribed right-of-way should be widened to include and preserve such natural features as ponds, streams, ravines, or groves of trees, as "furnishings" to the freeway.

39

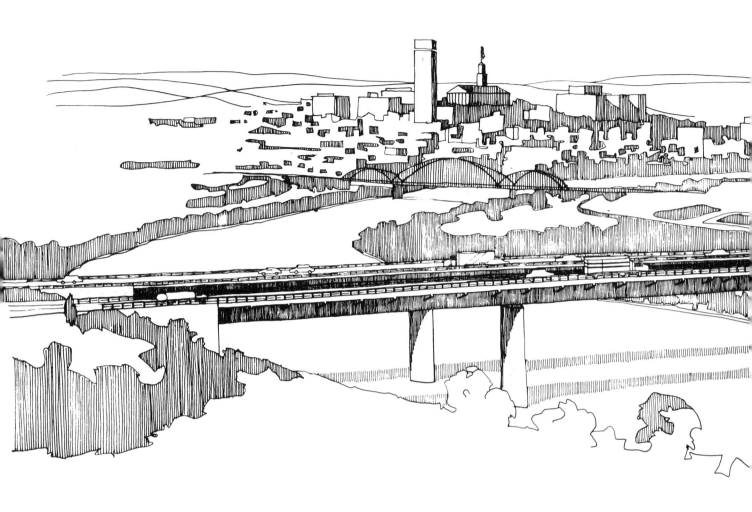

2/5

Freeways entering the city should, by their location and design, present each city in its most interesting light. Designed as dramatic gateways, they should differ in character and detail so that each is unique and gives visual orientation to both the city and the expressway.

They should provide a series of evolving views of the city's outstanding physical features. Much of what a citizen or visitor of the city sees or knows of a city is observed from its arterial highways. Such experiences should not be accidental. Pittsburgh's freeway approach to the Golden Triangle, the view of Manhattan from the Brooklyn-Queens Expressway, or of San Francisco from the Golden Gate Bridge are examples of the spectacular possibilities.

2/6

The driver and his passengers should be presented with a sequential and unfolding flow of attractive images. This is a relatively new type of visual experience. The views from the highway should not be abrupt or fragmented. As a vehicle moves into, through, or out of the city, its various features should be introduced, enframed, and so related to the viewer as to give him a sense of what the place is really about. Where feasible, curvilinear highway alignments, in comparison with long, straight tangents, provide more attractive and varied views.

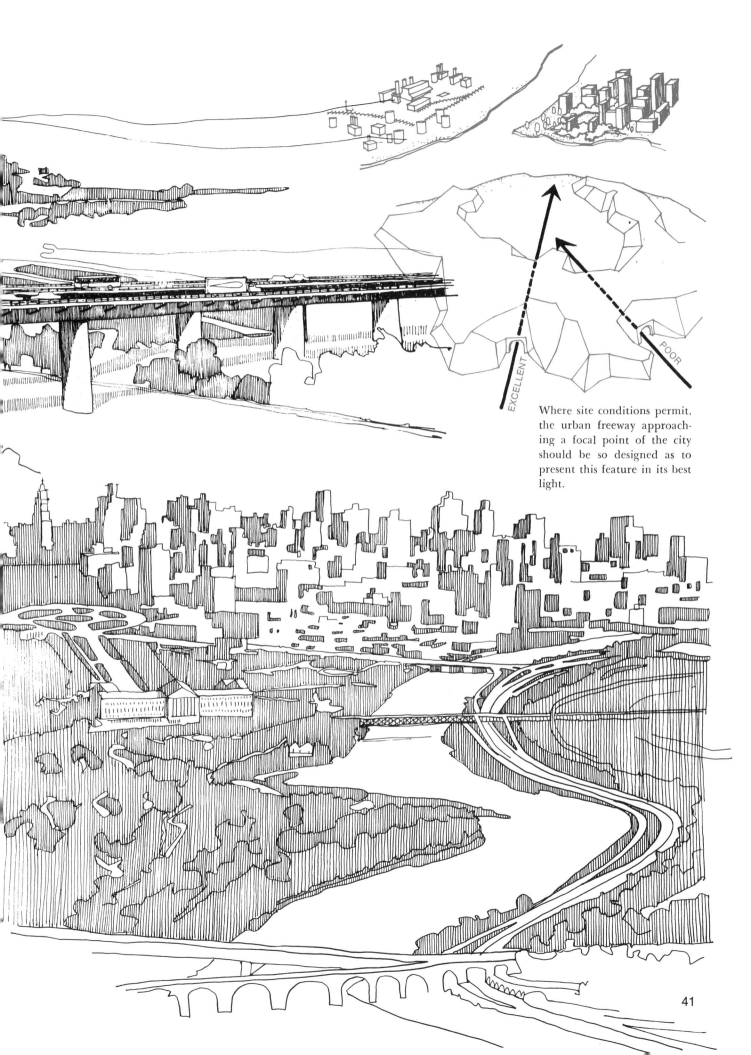

Where site conditions permit, the urban freeway approaching a focal point of the city should be so designed as to present this feature in its best light.

EXCELLENT

POOR

41

There must be a conscious effort to design attractive visual qualities into freeway location.

F. W. Cron has stated, "The study of visual qualities of alignment was not widespread until fairly recently. This is in spite of the proven esthetics and worth of these qualities in the parkways designed in and near American cities since the turn of the century and the German autobahns in the 1930's. However, in several highway departments in the 1930's and since, a continuing effort has been made to devise more satisfying roadway geometry. In doubtful situations models have been constructed, even though some were little more than three-dimensional strings on pegs. But the will is there. While many older highways show evidence of good visual result only by chance, recent decades have brought into widespread use photogrammetry, spline use, three-dimensional vision, models, and the application of landscape architectural principles."

The freeway should make the most of specific features of the cityscape. It is not enough that landmarks, activity centers, and topographic superlatives be left undisturbed. The freeway should relate to each in such a way as to identify and reveal to the motorist its special character. Where the highway passes close to an historic landmark, the highway improvement should include screening where this is indicated, or the development of an appropriate foreground and enframement of the feature as viewed from the road.

On a freeway, the visual effects will be comprehensible to its users only if their high speed of travel is borne in mind. Compared to streets, expressways require a very different scale. Signs, views, and variations in grade or alignment and landscape development must be designed to the viewer's trajectory, speed, and range of perceptual capability.

It is to be noted that while the driver's line of sight lies in a narrow frontal sector, his passengers have a much wider viewing range.

The driver of a vehicle traveling at relatively high speed can only experience those views positioned almost directly ahead of him. "The driver's eyes are focused on the road ahead and his attention centers on his driving. Only for very short glimpses can he safely take his eyes from the road, and these can be only a few degrees to the right or left. As vehicle speed increases, the driver's eyes focus farther and farther ahead, and his angle of vision becomes narrower and narrower. At 25 miles per hour his total horizontal angle of vision is about $50°$ to either side, and the eyes focus at a point about 600 feet ahead, but for 60 miles per hour the focus may be nearly 2,000 feet ahead, while the angle of vision has shrunk to less than $20°$."—F. W. Cron

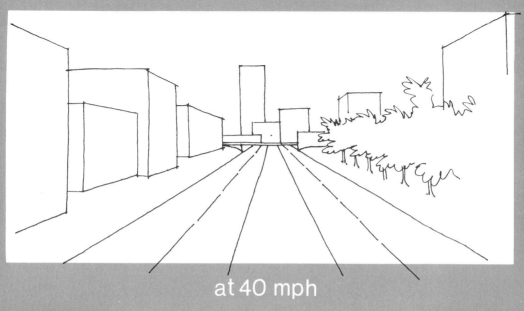

at 40 mph

at 50 mph

at 60 mph

The greater the speed of the vehicle, the farther ahead its driver is trying to see. This narrows his angle of vision, something a road-designer should keep in mind.

2/11

Views or objects in the middle distance as seen from a high-speed vehicle should be featured. By manipulation of freeway alignment, grade, and enframement they should be given sustained viewing time and importance.

Mountains, lakes, bridges, or towers are enjoyed as individual features. Smaller units are grouped by the eye into simple masses and comprehended by color, texture, and outline. Objects in the foreground whiz by out of focus.

2/12

Intermediate and near views assume much greater importance for lower speed roads. This is because the driver's normal length of focus is nearer and his angle of vision is wider. Also, since he is moving at lower speeds he has more time to perceive the view. Most of the really good scenic roads or parkways have comparatively low speeds.

2/13

What is seen of an expressway from the city is as important as what is seen of the city from the expressway. Visual aspects of arterial highway location and design should be considered from the points of view both of the user and of the communities traversed, generally favoring the group most affected in any specific instance. For example, an expressway in a scenic corridor should favor the user while a freeway in a built-up section of the city might favor residential neighbors.

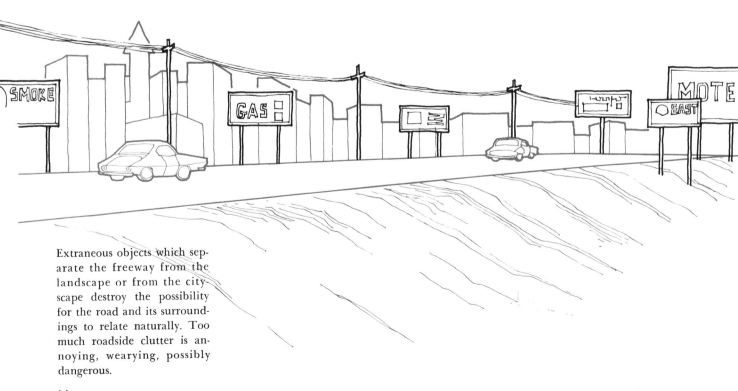

Extraneous objects which separate the freeway from the landscape or from the cityscape destroy the possibility for the road and its surroundings to relate naturally. Too much roadside clutter is annoying, wearying, possibly dangerous.

2/14

While the expressway in rural and suburban areas can harmonize with the elements of nature, an urban expressway must harmonize with architecture, and at best may be architecture. In the dense city, freeways may well be incorporated in architectural complexes, or may be suspended from tower structures.

2/15

When possible a roadway should be so located, designed, and controlled as to help eliminate unsightly features. Borrow pits, strip mines, and sanitary fills through which or beside which the urban highway moves can often be developed into roadside parks, recreation, or other use areas as part of the joint highway-urban building process.

2/16

In all highway planning there should be continuous and comprehensive evaluation of the terrain features of the entire urban area, not just a route reconnaissance of the single highway. Every opportunity should be taken to utilize, protect, and accentuate the site and terrain features which offer distinctive quality to the urban development.

2/17

Freeway design should be responsive to all the visual features and landmarks—both positive and negative—along projected routings. An inventory should be made to include all those natural and man-made features within a broad strip which can contribute to the making of a beautiful highway. Included should be a consideration of views and areas for essential landscape development. Rights-of-way should be widened where feasible to include features as permanent elements of the highway.

2/18

So far as visual quality in highway design is concerned, the best solutions are "natural" solutions. These include the rolling of the highway with or around (rather than across or through) attractive topographical features. Scars resulting from road cuts should be minimized. Attractive natural landscape elements such as marshes, hills, and groves should be preserved and featured rather than destroyed.

2/19

By its horizontal and vertical alignment an expressway may be made to "bring out" the best features of the landscape traversed. To "head into" rather than away from those views which are outstanding; to fall toward those features of interest on the base plane; to rise toward those features best seen from below or in silhouette against the sky—these are marks of superior highway alignment.

3

Location
of
the freeway

When citizens crowd into City Hall to speak with feeling about a proposed expressway, they are mainly concerned with its location and the consequent effect on their community. This is what the controversy over urban freeways is mostly about.

In the location of urban expressways, as of state trunk highways, various criteria are used to analyze alternatives, but in actual practice the economic considerations have too often been decisive.

Cost is a formidable factor. A highway department with more demands than budget is bound to be dollar conscious, and should be. But within a developed urban area in particular, the ability to move a maximum volume of vehicles from one area to another at the least mileage cost should be only one of several considerations. If preserving a community's integrity means going two miles farther, then major attention should be given to that alternative.

The urban freeway will normally be much more expensive, mile for mile, than its rural counterpart; this is inevitable if the freeway is to realize its full potential role in the city.

Part of the problem has been that the construction of large-scale urban freeways is relatively new. Highway engineers have not been given the legal authority or funds to go much beyond the more elementary kind of facility. Another part of the problem has been that many significant criteria such as social and esthetic values and effect on long-range planning cannot presently be quantified and thus plugged into a formula and readily weighed.

Only occasionally have the best minds in related disciplines been brought to bear on the highway planning and location process. They must be. It is not possible to make vital decisions in highway location by totaling up and comparing formula answers. Subjective evaluations always must be applied. But at the same time the use of new and highly successful techniques of analysis and decision-making must be expanded.

3/1

Urban expressway as well as all highway location should be based upon a survey of all determinants. These include but are not limited to:

Traffic desire lines
Topographic features
Existing and planned transportation facilities
Safety
Operation and maintenance costs
Acquisition and development costs
Social, economic, and political structures
Ecological factors
Historical features
Present and projected land uses and traffic ways
The architectural structure of the city and region
Permanent areas and features to remain
Areas where redevelopment or change is desirable
Scenic opportunities

3/2

Urban expressways should be so located as to respond fully to the existing city pattern and to describe for the metropolitan area a complete and workable system for reasonably high-speed traffic movement. A city or region may have one or more nuclei. Where several exist they may be of varying character and uses—as commercial, industrial, residential, recreational, or other. They may be grouped in varying arrangements—as in a ring, linear, as a constellation, or as satellites. These nuclei, together with their supporting land use areas and major traffic connections and bypasses, form the basic pattern. Only if this basic pattern is sound can the expressways function well.

3/3

Outer belt freeways should be considered as classifiers, giving choice of routes to districts or centers. Their sections and interchanges should be developed so as to accommodate rapid and smooth traffic flow.

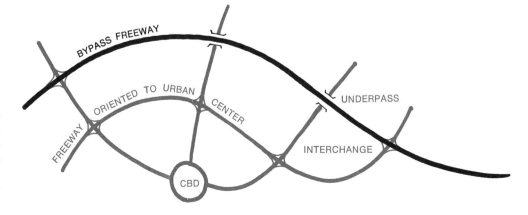

Some freeways are intended to serve drivers within cities, and others are meant to help drivers avoid cities. The two different intents can seldom be well combined. The added outer bypass loop is the solution.

3/4

The inner belt freeway should be so located as to serve as an interceptor, to receive and distribute traffic or divert it. The circumferential-radial freeway and major thoroughfare pattern, adjusted to topography and the city structure, provides cities with one of the most effective and efficient systems of traffic distribution.

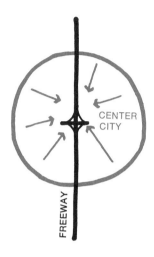

An interchange *within* an urban center requires that people drive *inward* in order to get *out*.

Where interchanges are located *outside* the urban center, and where local streets are adequate, traffic ingress and egress moves more efficiently and logically.

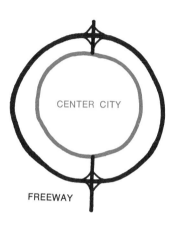

A circumferential expressway of six lanes (three lanes in each direction) saves land in the center of the city, and preserves local streets for local traffic.

3/5

If, all other possibilities having been explored, an arterial highway must pass through the heart of a city or central business district, then it should have few or no entrances or exits within the CBD. The essence of a central business district is its concentration of services and facilities. That this concentration, and thus the district's vitality, is lessened by the freeway occupancy is unfortunate. Additional land occupancy by ramps or interchanges may be fatal.

3/6

The best arterial routes are those that cause the least damage to existing communities and at the same time provide good traffic service at reasonable cost. Logical possibilities for freeway location in urbanized regions include active or vacated transit routes, strips or wedges of undeveloped land, blighted areas subject to redevelopment, fill or borrow areas, eroded lands, and flood plains (on elevated roadways). Other possibilities include borders of public and/or institutional holdings, corridors through developing commercial or industrial districts as a welcome spine, or along the edges of water bodies where their presence would by alignment and section be compatible with adjacent uses.

296-930 O - 68 - 4

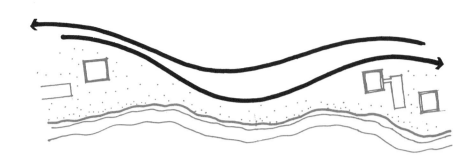

A freeway may skirt a river without excluding other riverside land uses. The highway may be swung close to the water for the view, then moved away to allow other land uses.

NECESSARY ACQUISITION

FREEWAY

Whenever the existing street pattern is regular and dense the freeway must either be constructed parallel to the established streets or it must bear the cost of increased property-taking, damages and redevelopment.

Even in America few cities have consistent grid patterns, but are, rather, comprised of series of grids. Freeway alignment, at best, will respond to each grid series. Sufficient right-of-way should be acquired, where feasible, to provide transitional areas, sometimes in the form of green parklike boundaries between the adjacent street patterns.

3/7

In the location and design of a highway its effect on contiguous community areas in terms of noise and fumes may be an important factor. Where annoyance factors are critical an alternate highway location may be indicated. With any given alignment, however, the effect of noise and fumes may be greatly reduced by careful design of the section, utilization of elevation or depression, treatment of surfaces, and use of sound and fume absorptive trees.

3/8

Urban freeways should follow the grid or grain of the city. In those areas of the city where strong geometric and district patterns have been established freeways should be aligned in harmony with these patterns; otherwise they will cut across and disrupt the neighborhoods and their trafficways.

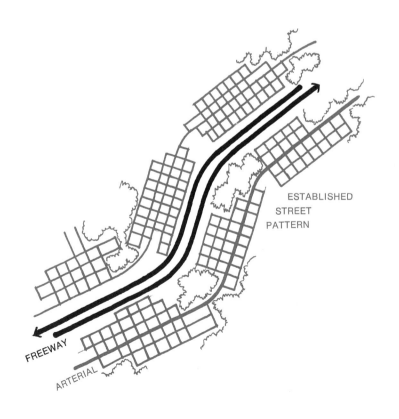

ESTABLISHED
STREET
PATTERN

FREEWAY

ARTERIAL

3/9

A freeway may well be a boundary but should never be a barrier between communities. When a freeway is treated as a line of demarcation a sufficient number of grade separated crossings must be provided to assure free and easy intercommunication.

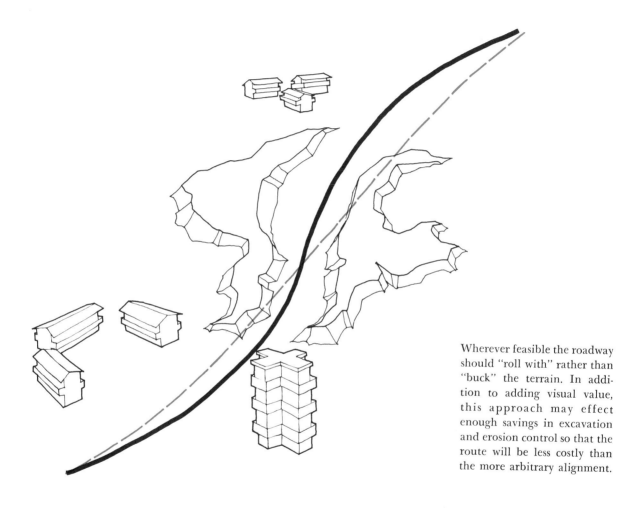

Wherever feasible the roadway should "roll with" rather than "buck" the terrain. In addition to adding visual value, this approach may effect enough savings in excavation and erosion control so that the route will be less costly than the more arbitrary alignment.

3/10

Expressway location must be responsive to natural forces. An expressway, like a building, must be designed in studied relationship to topographical features, the sweep of the sun, the force and direction of the storms and winds, and with all microclimatological and ecological factors in mind.

3/11

Highways divided as two one-way roadways, each independent of the other, almost invariably result in better fit than uniform median design. Where the overall massiveness of the roadways is a problem in relation to the character of the areas through which they pass, and where land space is available, the two roadways should be widely separated, perhaps blocks apart.

3/12

In planning the urban highway in relation to dominant topographic forms or man-made structures, the roadway should be so aligned and constructed as to preserve and accentuate the best qualities of the landscape. Attractive and interesting land forms should not be hacked away to provide a roadbed.

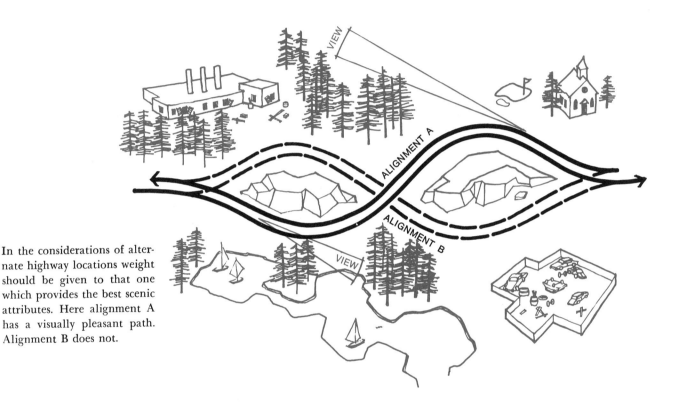

In the considerations of alternate highway locations weight should be given to that one which provides the best scenic attributes. Here alignment A has a visually pleasant path. Alignment B does not.

3/13

Where appropriate and feasible, highways may well be located adjacent to or upon natural or man-made barriers such as rivers, bluffs, hillsides, railroads, or other transit routes. Roads that run parallel to and in harmony with such linear features are often less expensive, require fewer crossings, and leave intact more existing development. Piers should be slender; slopes should be terraced.

3/14

The placement of transportation and transit routes within a common corridor is often advantageous. Since both are linear routes of movement serving the metropolitan region, a common right-of-way provides obvious benefits of location, land taking, and joint construction.

JOINT FREEWAY-TRANSIT RIGHT-OF-WAY

FREEWAY   TRANSITWAY   FREEWAY

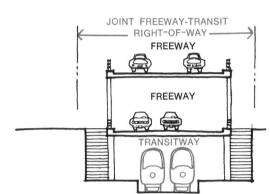

JOINT FREEWAY-TRANSIT
RIGHT-OF-WAY
FREEWAY

FREEWAY

TRANSITWAY

When a rail transit line is run down the middle of a freeway, it becomes an island separated from its passengers by rivers of automobiles. If it runs down one side of the freeway, the transit line may still be separated from half its passengers. Access by pedestrian bridge or tunnel is costly and indirect. An obviously better solution is to stack the expressway lanes on top the transit line, resulting in a narrower right of way. An additional level for crosswise traffic of vehicles and pedestrians would complete the equation for easy movement.

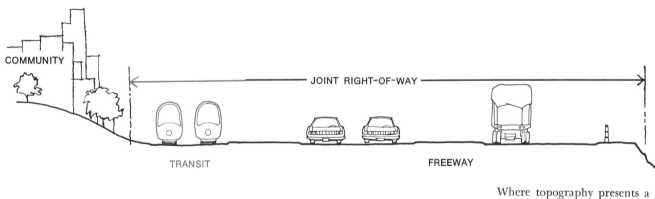

COMMUNITY

JOINT RIGHT-OF-WAY

TRANSIT   FREEWAY

Where topography presents a natural deterrent to development on one side of a transit-transportation right-of-way, transit can be related directly to community needs.

TRANSIT
STATION

COMMUNITY

When the community lies to one side only of a transit-transportation way the transit facilities may be manipulated by alignment or grade to relate directly to the community.

53

The roadway

The urban freeway differs in many ways from its rural counterpart. An understanding of these differences is fundamental to urban roadway design. A highway that is poorly planned and designed is a misfortune anywhere, but a far graver one in the city. All the negative effects are automatically magnified: air pollution, noise, disruption of neighborhoods and of peoples' lives—and traffic volumes are drastically increased, with loads fluctuating morning and evening in almost tidal proportions. Even the visual character of an urban highway matters more than that of a rural one, for the reason that it is seen by more people.

In fact the basic situation is so different, and so difficult, that inevitably we will be led to wholly new types of freeways—new forms and sections, and new concepts of vehicular movement and of vehicles themselves. The urban freeway must be designed as a scientifically contrived space through which the motorist or truck driver may move speedily, safely, and freely, enjoying a landscape designed to keep him relaxed and at the same time alert. This calls for new ways to integrate highways with other facilities and with the three-dimensional structure of the city. In the words of former Federal Highway Administrator Rex Whitton, "We are groping for solutions; imagination and vision are at a premium."

4/1

Means must be found by which the sheer area and mass of the freeway may be reduced to a more human scale. One of the most objectionable features of our expressways is their vast and overwhelming size compared to the normal street.

4/2

Urban freeways should often be condensed and concentrated. In heavily developed cores of the city they should use multilevel, split-level, cantilevered, depressed, and elevated cross sections to yield a concentration of traffic flow within a narrow right-of-way.

As a byproduct, connections across freeways from one side to the other may become much easier to achieve.

4/3

Compact interchanges should be considered for major urban intersections. Such structures, designed for the purpose, greatly reduce the land takings in critical areas of the central city.

4/4

Arterial highway lanes may be separated horizontally as well as vertically. In the interest of lower acquisition and construction costs, as well as improved operation, in some conditions, it is better to have widely spaced and separate roadways for the various types and directions of traffic.

4/5

Expressway, local, and pedestrian traffic should be separated either by level, by distance, or by structural barrier. A place must be provided for each. Each must be well suited to its function and all must be well interrelated.

In the high-rise city a lower level might serve contiguous garage structures; the next higher might provide local traffic movement; and the highest level might carry through traffic only.

4/6

A hillside section of an urban highway should be designed as a terraced structure providing for the movement and storage of vehicles in close proximity to urban concentrations. Such structures—freestanding, laid back against a hill or bluff, or integrated with linear buildings—are part of a new concept of freeway design.

The presence of trucks in the ordinary traffic stream adds tension and subtracts efficiency for automobile drivers.

4/7

For some conditions urban freeways should provide a separate lane for slow-moving trucks. Where freight carriers and passenger vehicles use a common highway, the carrying capacity can be significantly increased when an extra and designated truck lane is provided. Where a separate lane is not feasible for long distances it can at least be installed to advantage on the long uphill stretches.

4/8

Freeways should never have more than eight lanes in one corridor, with four lanes in each direction. Where greater capacity is required an additional freeway some distance away is preferable to an increase in width or number of lanes.

Expressways should drive past, rather than slice through, the central business district or other high-density areas, providing several choices of ingress and egress. Good practice often provides an inner freeway loop or major thoroughfare loop to intercept traffic and distribute it to and around the central business district. The freeway loop should be related to an internal circulation and distribution street system which interconnects it with terminal parking facilities at the periphery of the central core.

The area outside the inner loop can well be designated as urban park with high density residential uses, less expensive parking, and with ready access to the central business district.

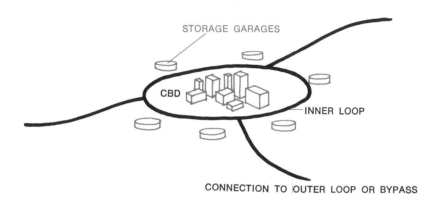

STORAGE GARAGES

CBD

INNER LOOP

CONNECTION TO OUTER LOOP OR BYPASS

The essence of a thriving central business district (CBD) is compression, with convenient access. The way to achieve both is to provide an inner loop freeway ringing the CBD, and to add parking facilities around the loop.

All freeways should provide a continuous shoulder on both sides of each roadway for disabled vehicles. No moving vehicles should be separated from a pulloff shoulder by more than one traffic lane. Both the safety of the highway users and the elimination of tieups are involved. Where a continuous shoulder strip is not feasible, frequent emergency pulloff bays should be provided.

Freeways with reversible center roadways offer an effective means of handling peak hour traffic. Where traffic moves into and out of cities in surges, with dominant morning and evening directional peaks, the alternating traffic lanes provide for maximum flow on minimum space.

It may prove feasible for urban highways subject to the dangers and discomforts of weather extremes to be covered with translucent or illuminated roofs, climate-controlled, or equipped with snow melting equipment. Such treatment, of course, need not and should not be generally applied. There are many situations, however, where protection from snow and ice, or from sun, glare, fog, and rain would improve the levels of both safety and efficiency.

4/13

Whenever partial interchanges are designed, they should be studied for ultimate conversion into full interchanges. Sufficient right-of-way should be acquired in anticipation of the time when increased traffic or changed traffic patterns make their reconstruction necessary.

There are cases where formidable natural or man-made barriers, or the lack of future traffic generation potential, may make a full interchange unfeasible. Otherwise, provision for four-way interconnection should be made.

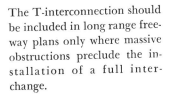

PARTIAL
INTERCHANGE

MAJOR BARRIER

The T-interconnection should be included in long range freeway plans only where massive obstructions preclude the installation of a full interchange.

4/14

A freeway system should provide continuity. Both by its sustained carrying capacity and by its route each segment must be considered as a working part of a coherent inter-regional system of vehicular traffic movement. Abrupt changes in capacity or alignment should be precluded.

4/15

Freeways projected into any land area should not be dead-ended. They should be so planned and scheduled that each segment when completed will provide direct two-way connection with the regional freeway network.

Regional freeway spurs should not be left without through connections but should provide a fully interconnected segment in each construction phase.

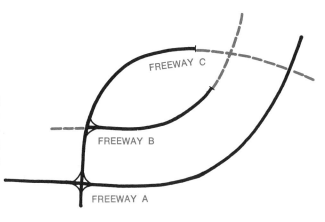

FREEWAY C

FREEWAY B

FREEWAY A

4/16

In highways traversing urban areas the full possibilities of new construction techniques should be explored. Alternatives include the use of open-cut freeways with partial cover, open-section tunnels, cut and cover near-surface tunnels, underground tunnels, elevated structures, and architecturally integrated roadways.

New high-speed drilling techniques, improved sections, ventilation, and lighting will make the use of tunnels more feasible. New materials and methods of construction will also produce more attractive viaducts of lighter section.

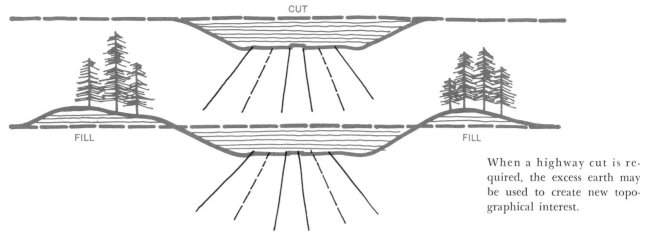

CUT

FILL   FILL

When a highway cut is required, the excess earth may be used to create new topographical interest.

4/17

The grading of the expressway right-of-way has much to do with its quality. It is now common practice to use fairly flat slopes for cuts and fills and to mold these slopes into the natural contours of the terrain. This is "contour grading" of the highway. The use of naturally shaped, or architectural, embankments for screening or enframement will be a logical and fitting extension of this trend.

4/18

Highway cuts and fills, with their scars on the landscape, may be reduced by the use of retaining walls. Sensitive roadway location, or even minor vertical or horizontal adjustment of the centerline, may substantially reduce the resultant cuts and fills and the destruction of natural cover. Long hillside gashes or raw notches seen against the sky may often be eliminated by short tunnels. In scenic areas and particularly in cities the increased costs are clearly justified.

4/19

In good alignment there is a direct and essential relationship between horizontal and vertical curvature. Where the design includes both, a change of profile should be related to change in horizontal curvature and should occur at or near the beginning or end of horizontal curves.

To achieve a visually harmonious road alignment there must be a carefully considered relationship between horizontal flow and vertical curvature. Generally the high or low point of a vertical curve should coincide with the midpoint of a horizontal curve.

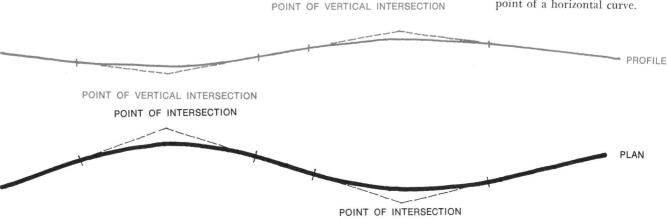

POINT OF VERTICAL INTERSECTION

POINT OF VERTICAL INTERSECTION

POINT OF INTERSECTION

PROFILE

PLAN

POINT OF INTERSECTION

4/20

Short horizontal and vertical curves should be avoided, especially if the central angle is small. For satisfactory appearance a vertical or horizontal curve should be at least 1,000 feet long.

4/21

Spiral transition curves improve the appearance of curved alignments. To be visually significant the spirals should be much longer than the minimum required for the control speed to accomplish the transition from tangent to curve.

4/22

Appropriate right-of-way planting is important as a means of screening unsightly views and enframing urban superlatives. It is also useful in dust control, noise abatement, the provision of windbreaks, and the prevention of headlight glare.

While planting can help make the city more attractive and blend the freeway into its urban environment, its use should never be mistaken for a meaningful answer to those aspects of expressways which are not functionally graceful.

4/23

Urban freeway planting should normally be limited to ground cover for erosion control and to drifts of native shade and flowering trees. Detail is lost to the high-speed traveller. Small plantings seem to clutter. Pleasantly swelling ground planes and strong tree masses are more effective.

It must be remembered that trees or ground cover will grow only with sufficient rainfall, or where irrigation can be built in. Wherever possible, the original plant cover should be saved and volunteer growth encouraged after the roadway construction is completed.

Freeway plantings should generally be comprised of trees arranged as they might grow naturally, in great drifts or masses. The best results are often those produced by judicious highway alignment and grading which preserves existing growth. While specimen trees or clumps may well be used for screening, framing views, or as free standing focal points, the indiscriminate use of scattered exotic "decorative" plantings is seldom effective.

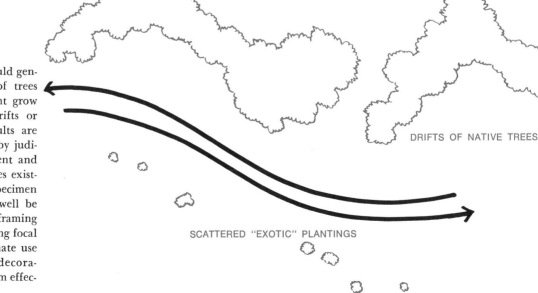

DRIFTS OF NATIVE TREES

SCATTERED "EXOTIC" PLANTINGS

4/24

Roadside landscape improvements usually reduce maintenance costs. Quite apart from their appearance, such improvements as the flattening and rounding of slopes, seeding, erosion control, and indigenous landscape planting have produced significant savings in maintenance budgets. Other devices, such as flat fill slopes which increase the driver's chances of survival if he leaves the roadway, and median plantings which inhibit glare, may be justified as much by safety as by esthetic value.

4/25

It is important to the scenic quality of expressways of parkway character that the area at the intersection of tangents for a highway curve be expanded to widen the right-of-way. This will permit the development of viewing enframement or foreground and prevent the erection of billboards or other structures which might block the view.

4/26

In urban residential areas, as in the open countryside, protective right-of-way fencing should be hidden behind the tree line wherever possible. This insistent and obtrusive fence line in the landscape can be softened or completely screened with plantings. This is particularly important on sidehill shoulders or terrain crests where the fence would otherwise "read" against the sky.

4/27

Application of established surveillance and control techniques should be extended and further developed. Surveillance, or observation, of the freeway is usually accomplished by electronic instrumentation such as vehicle detectors, digital or analog computers, closed-circuit television, and weather detectors. Control normally implies the altering of the behavior of vehicles on or before entering the freeway. It may be applied by ramp closure or metering. It may be aided by the use of informational signs.

Prototype installations, while limited and remedial in nature, have been effective. They can be much more effective when they are more comprehensive and planned in advance. Research should include particularly an investigation of methods of controlling route selection through diversion to alternative freeway or arterial routes and the effect of such control on freeway system design.

4/28

Speeds should be lower in central core areas. Decreased speeds permit greater conformity to the typical grid pattern, reduction of curve radii, interchange sizes, and land areas required, and provide greater flexibility in location and design.

4/29

Speed limits on an urban expressway system should be regulated according to location and pressure of traffic. Minimum as well as maximum speeds should be enforced.

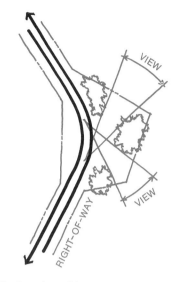

The location of freeway curvatures should be related to views and other visual attractions. Additional right of way should be acquired at those intersections where it is needed in order to secure adequate foreground and enframement for outstanding views.

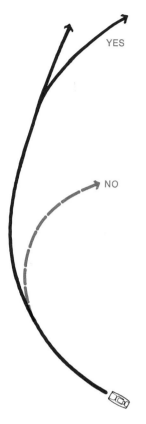

As the driver's decision-making time factor is increased, both safety and driving pleasure are also increased.

4/30

Freeways by their alignment, grade, and volumetric characteristics should provide an experience of free-flowing movement. Constrictions, abrupt changes of course, and other mechanical or visual disruptions should be avoided.

4/31

A new approach to highway safety must emerge from a scientific analysis of the user's experiences—his psychological and physiological reactions to each of the highway's environmental elements and their sum total. In this regard it has been noted by many that safety is a byproduct of esthetic factors. The Garden State Parkway, in New Jersey, for example, is safe at least in part because it was designed from the scenic point of view. It features long sweeping curves instead of tangents, variation in tree-enframed spaces rather than evenly spaced trees with their soporific rhythm, constant change of rolling topography rather than flat-graded roadbeds and mechanically sloped cuts and embankments, and a carefully planned sequence of attractive forward views. Monotony means boredom and danger. Variety keeps the driver alert, and increases his factor of safety.

4/32

Multichoice route decisions should be eliminated wherever possible. Where this is not feasible the signs should give clear, advance, and repeated directional information. Safety is diminished and lane capacity drastically reduced when the drivers of high-speed vehicles are forced to make quick decisions in the choice of one of several possible routes.

4/33

Widened medians and separation of roadways reduce the hazard of collisions. While wider medians require added right -of-way width they are often attained without additional cost when the increased width allows for slope differentiation in grades and thus reduces cuts and embankments. Visually separated roadways usually have the advantages of improved scale, reduced grading, and more scenic qualities in addition to added safety.

The expressway right-of-way (especially in residential or renewal areas) can often be expanded to include the feeder street with a park strip in between. The cost of the additional land and park strip *and* feeder street may well be less than that for connecting ramps from each major local street.

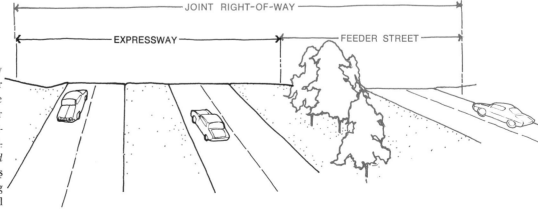

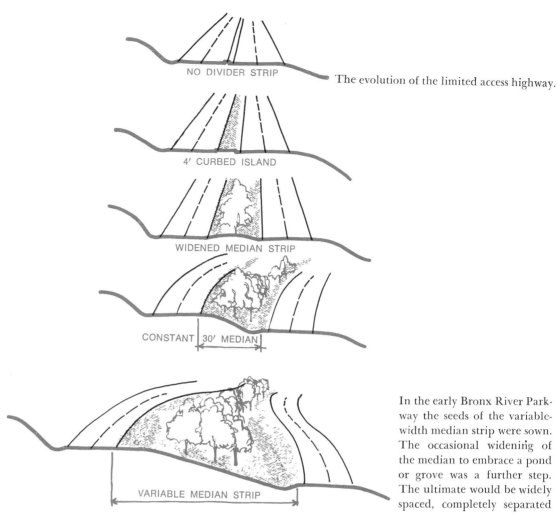

NO DIVIDER STRIP

4' CURBED ISLAND

WIDENED MEDIAN STRIP

CONSTANT 30' MEDIAN

VARIABLE MEDIAN STRIP

The evolution of the limited access highway.

In the early Bronx River Parkway the seeds of the variable-width median strip were sown. The occasional widening of the median to embrace a pond or grove was a further step. The ultimate would be widely spaced, completely separated one-way roadways.

4/34

Highway shoulders and adjacent roadsides should be designed to allow clear recovery area for the drivers of vehicles which are out of control. Roadside sections and treatment should be so developed as to minimize vehicle damage and passenger injury and to provide an environment for decelerating the out-of-control vehicle.

This, emphatically, does not mean that clear roadwide strips of uniform width and section must be provided. Many highway consulting firms have been so geared to a high production schedule and rigid application of fixed dimensional criteria that their design process makes impossible any sensitive response to existing topography or other environmental factors. An essential ingredient of superior highway design is a thoughtful, flexible-minded approach which can make the most of a clear right-of-way possibility attainable at reasonable cost while yet providing the undulating slopes and variable treelines which make for a handsome roadway.

It is urged that the recent AASHO and BPR recommendation, made in the interest of safety, proposing a 30' clear roadside width with 6:1 side slopes, be restated to emphasize a variable roadside design rather than a stereotyped cross section. Otherwise, this proposal (which in some states has been considered a mandatory requirement) would cost untold millions of dollars in increased grading and bridge costs, if rigidly adhered to, and would produce thousands of miles of monotonous highways.

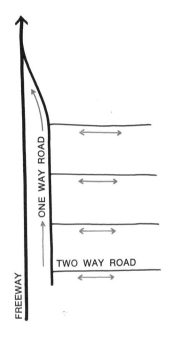

The urban freeway must be supplemented with nonfrontage service roads which provide frequent connections to the major local streets. Local traffic should be collected on a feeder road so that one adequately sized ramp connection can be built, rather than many.

4/35

A well designed highway should provide a sense of containment and spatial modulation. The freeway section should be compressed where topography so dictates and expanded where structures, land forms, or views so suggest. It is desirable that the highway sometimes move through narrow passages between buildings or through ravines or tight rocky cut sections. It should provide swelling ground forms and undulating edge treatment to accentuate the sense of expanding-contracting containment and to keep the driver interested and alert.

On a fill section there is no reason not to bring tree planting to the back of the guardrail and let high branches overhang the shoulders. The foliage and shadows would do much to add pleasure and interest to the experience of driving. Many parkways designed on this principle have exemplary safety records.

4/36

The design and placement of signs and other structures should provide all possible safety features. Rigid posts at the roadway edge have contributed to many fatal collisions. Breakaway posts for signs and lights would reduce this hazard. Massive structures have often been located in off-ramp areas at the very point where driver error frequently occurs. The installation of guardrails to deflect vehicles from direct impact has not been fully effective. Promising energy-absorbing devices should be used instead.

4/37

In many cases the local streets of a CBD can be advantageously collected into a service, or collector-distributor, street before joining the expressway by ramp. The direct connection of numerous local streets into the freeway disrupts traffic flow and reduces efficiency and safety.

4/38

On and off ramps to streets should be divorced from freeway to freeway interchanges. The location of local access or egress ramps should be well removed from the primary interchange. Otherwise the driver is confronted with too many confusing choices of route and too many quick decisions.

4/39

Freeway exit names should be short and descriptive of their destination. The more direct and the more comprehensible the nomenclature and signing the more effective they will be.

4/40

Continuing research should be devoted to the development of scientific guidelines in highway signage. The projection of directional guidance through visual and audio devices is presently in a rudimentary stage. When perfected, techniques will surpass our most advanced current navigational procedures and provide the driver with constantly available data on his position in relation to destination, turning points, and hazardous conditions.

4/41

For all freeways major consideration should be given to color coding and further standardization of signing structures, shapes, sizes, lettering, and symbols. Indeed, complete re-evaluation of methods and standards should take place on a frequent periodic basis.

4/42

All automobile radios should be provided with a special channel on which official area highway information can be received. New official broadcasting systems would provide information on weather, highway conditions, traffic congestion, and suggested alternate routes. In the near future it could also include automatic control systems.

4/43

There should be expanded and intensive research on post-accident factors including the detection of accidents, bringing emergency equipment to the scene, and removing the injured. Specific subjects would include:

The use of median and shoulder design to provide space for the movement of emergency vehicles.

Location and practicability of emergency entrances and exits to enable traffic to bypass the accident area.

Automatic changeable message signs and/or radio communication systems to provide accident information indicating alternate bypass routes around accident-blocked highway sections.

Deployment by air of investigative, medical, and cleanup teams to reduce the time required for accident investigation, emergency care and removal of the injured, and removal of damaged vehicles.

Methods of highway design that will make provision for future maintenance and repair of highway facilities without creating conditions that produce accidents or congestion.

4/44

Driving regulations and enforcement procedures must be established according to objective facts for the whole of the urban region. These should be generally uniform from state to state, and community to community, enforced with justice, and modified as warranted by new conditions and new knowledge.

4/45

All levels of government should work together to advance highway safety. The present government structures of nearly all large metropolitan regions are fragmented to such an extent that inter- and intra-governmental cooperation is minimal; federal allocation of funds should be contingent on intergovernmental cooperation on a prescribed basis and to achieve prescribed results.

Highway structures

The design of advanced and distinguished bridges, tunnels, lighting systems, signs, and other physical appurtenances of the modern freeway presents a particular challenge to creative effort in this country. For the truth is that the preponderance of new ideas in this area over the past century has come from Western Europe, despite U.S. engineering leadership in electronics, mechanics, and aerodynamics.

We can benefit from a close study of European work, as well as our own. Indeed, who today would be so brash as to undertake the design of a major concrete bridge without studying the structures of Robert Maillart and his disciples? Who would employ the use of cables in suspension unless he was familiar with their application in the bridges of John Augustus Roebling and the men who further developed his theories and techniques?

We can also benefit, in a more general way, from a very different kind of study: a consideration of the ways in which nature itself confronts and solves its design problems. In the words of the distinguished structural engineer, Fred M. Severud quoted in *Architectural Forum*, "Improbable as it may sound, it is a fact that the contemporary architect or engineer faces few problems in structural design which nature has not already met and solved. By our own standards, her designs are structurally more efficient and esthetically more satisfying than ours. We should—to paraphrase that forthright pre-Civil War critic, Horatio Greenough—learn from nature like men and not copy her like apes. But the truth of the matter is that we have only recently perfected the means whereby her structures can really be understood."

One thing is very clear: standards that go beyond the requirements of safety must be of the most general nature, and then issued as suggested guidelines only. Otherwise they become constrictors, stifling ideas, producing mediocre and conventional work. Imagination, constructive discontent, openmindedness, and self-confidence must be free to operate. Creativity should in all ways be encouraged, and innovations assiduously sought.

5/1

Esthetic value should have high priority in all highway structures. Their appearance from the highway and from its sides; their obstruction or enframement of views; their bulk and mass; their architectural character; their sculptural profile— all are important to those who will judge them in place. In every city from many viewing points highway structures are dominant. How they are designed will affect their communities for years.

5/2

The reality of a bridge lies in its structure. "Ordinarily the art of architectural or landscape design consists of the creation of space, and structure is finally a means to that end. But since the function of a bridge is simply the continuation of a roadway over a void, its structure is both means and end, and its reality lies not in space enclosed, but in structure itself. Since a bridge does not define space, but cuts through it, it is free of all the intricate psychological considerations that must be taken into account when space is molded or enclosed. Thus, paradoxically, a bridge is at once the most tangible and most abstract of architectural problems. As such, it is capable of extraordinary purity.

"The art of bridge building lies in the recognition and development of the beauty latent in those structural forms that most effectively exploit the strength and special properties of a given material."—ELIZABETH B. MOCK in *The Architecture of Bridges.*

5/3

Steel or concrete highway structures should not be faced with decorative metal panels or masonry veneer. Beauty in freeway design rises from a combination of careful planning, the direct and sensitive use of materials, and able detailing. Steel and concrete if expressively used are beautiful in themselves.

5/4

Bridges in a freeway system have both an individual and collective impact. Not only does each structure stand on its own merits, the whole system of structures makes, or ought to make, an architectural statement. A heterogeneity of bridge types and architectural styles, as seen in certain early parkway systems, is to be avoided.

5/5

An orderly pattern of overpass design in a freeway system is commendable. However, as conditions and requirements change, the structures should express the direct solution while maintaining uniformity of material, finish, detail, and furnishings.

5/6

When the scale or proportion of a bridge seems wrong, the fault is usually one of brutality. Even in a powerful landscape, where heavy structures might seem to be in keeping, the contrast of slender bridge members and profile is usually more

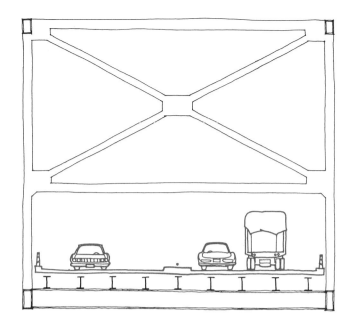
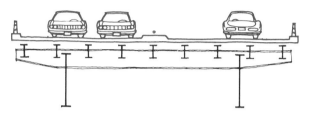

The bulky superstructure should give way to deck construction.

pleasing. Rather than strive for a contrived harmony of structure with its setting, it is often best to disturb the setting as little as possible.

5/7

Bridge designers should minimize the amount of superstructure above roadways. Deck bridges are inherently more attractive than through trusses and afford an unobstructed view of the surroundings.

5/8

Bridges which can be viewed as a thin ribbon or which show a light silhouette over the roadway or stream below generally create a pleasant impression. Subsidiary solid appurtenances, such as solid parapets or massive balusters across the span, should be avoided; they look like part of the load carrying structure and create the illusion of over-strength or gross structural over-dimensioning when viewed from below. Also, they obstruct the vision of the motorists.

The shallowest depth of structure consistent with strength and stiffness requirements, and with minimum clearances, should be used. Not only is this pleasing esthetically, but economically it is the best solution in complicated interchanges where compression of all the profiles will reduce the overall area of the interchange. An evaluation of costs in such situations must also consider the length and depth of approaches, wingwalls, and amount of property acquisition required by greater depths of construction.

5/9

Except for footbridges, excessive arching of the roadway profile over bridges is unnatural and inconsistent with high-speed motor travel. The roadway profile as it extends across the bridge should continue that of the approaches without break in grade, or with appropriately graceful vertical curvature.

5/10

Footbridges should be provided at key pedestrian crossing points. Above-grade pedestrian bridges are normally preferred to tunnel underpasses because of policing problems.

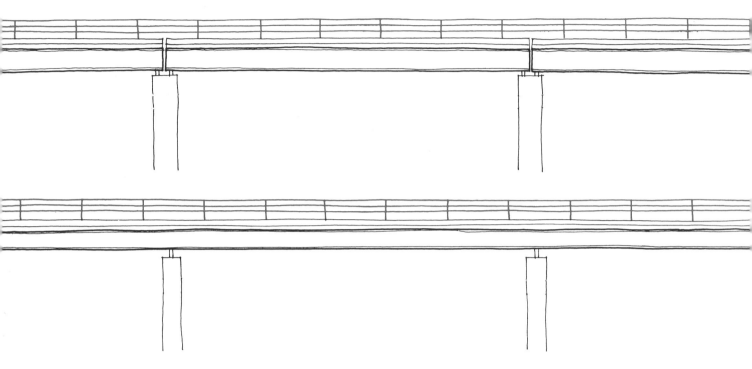

5/11

In bridge forms, particularly where multiple elements are involved, structural continuity unifies the system, making it both more efficient and more attractive. Most structures in nature are continuous, be they trees, leaves, morning glories, walnut shells, or spider webs. As it is in nature so is it also in highway structures.

5/12

Beam and girder spans with curved or segmentally haunched soffits are considered the closest analogue to nature's tree limbs, both in their physical vigor and technical effectiveness, and therefore a highly desirable esthetic form. Nonetheless, uniformity of depth of beam or girder bridges, either in simple or multiple-span arrangements, offers such clean lines and simplicity, plus advantages in fabrication and erection, that it must be considered equally acceptable, even though it lacks a strict counterpart in nature.

5/13

In multiple-span arrangements, particularly with large variations in span lengths, fascia girders should have comparable depths. Otherwise the total bridge will resemble a series of individual disconnected bridges rather than a unified whole.

5/14

Recently developed three-span continuous-frame girder bridges with inclined side column supports are efficient and attractive, and provide widths that give an added measure of safety to the motorist. The structural action in the frame approaches an arch in behavior. The dynamic form of the bridge is comparable to that of a lithe greyhound leaping over the road or stream below.

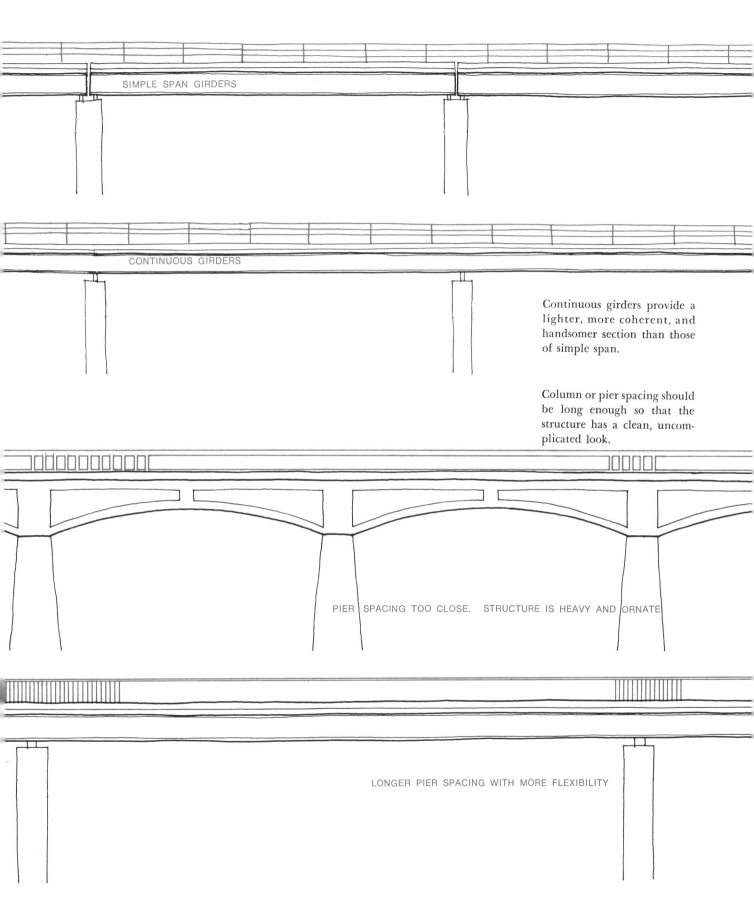

SIMPLE SPAN GIRDERS

CONTINUOUS GIRDERS

Continuous girders provide a lighter, more coherent, and handsomer section than those of simple span.

Column or pier spacing should be long enough so that the structure has a clean, uncomplicated look.

PIER SPACING TOO CLOSE.   STRUCTURE IS HEAVY AND ORNATE

LONGER PIER SPACING WITH MORE FLEXIBILITY

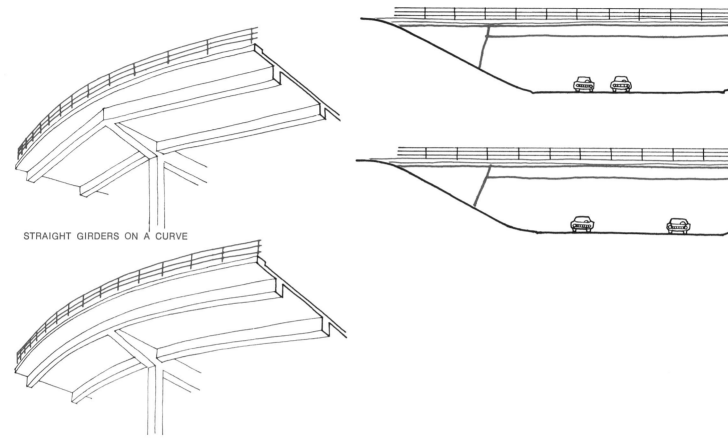

STRAIGHT GIRDERS ON A CURVE

GIRDERS CURVED TO FIT CURVE OF ROADWAY (PREFERRED)

Girders should, and can, follow the highway curve.

5/15

An overhead or through truss is economical and therefore widely used, but handsome examples are almost nonexistent. Nineteenth century bridges were composed of many light members which produced an airy weblike structure of well defined and handsome geometric planes. Contemporary trusses must be heavier to carry our heavier loads but they need not be bulky.

5/16

In flat terrain, an open type overpass structure with wide shoulders and side slopes is to be preferred over those types which produce a tunnel effect, as with rigid frames of limited span. In depressed freeways running between vertical retaining walls for considerable distances such openness obviously cannot be attained. In any case, the adequacy of the light under the bridge should be investigated and artificial light provided where required.

5/17

The structural diagram of a beautiful bridge will usually be readily comprehended by the observer. When the interplay of forces is most simply resolved and most directly expressed the result is most satisfying.

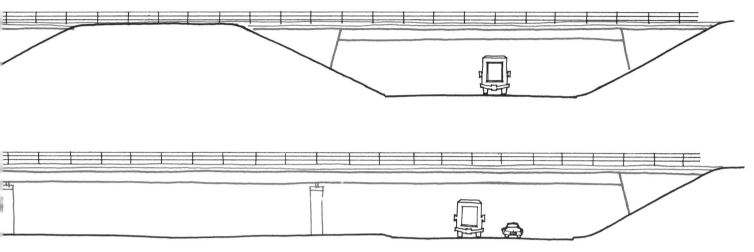

5/18

Where wide center medians are used between opposing traffic ways, the use of short pieces of embankment between two bridges crossing these lanes is incongruous. A continuous structure is the preferred and natural alternative.

5/19

Vertical alignment introducing a sagging vertical curve in the bridge produces an unfavorable structural appearance when viewed from the side or below. The eye is very sensitive to any deviation below a horizontal line of reference. Whether caused by a built-in sagging curvature or by a structural deflection due to load, such deviations tend to be distorted in magnitude.

5/20

Consideration should be given to the appearance of the underside of bridges or other overhead structures. These surfaces become visibly important when approached from a highway below and on an ascending grade.

Earth embankments separating bridges at wide center malls should be avoided. Instead, the two spans should be combined into a continuous structure.

The underside of a roadway must be designed as carefully as the top side, when it is elevated. Here the supports are shapely and widely spaced.

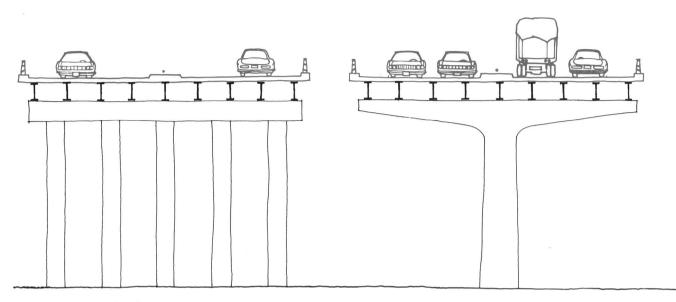

Elevated freeways no longer need be designed like docks on piling. Instead the roadways can be held up by a row of graceful central supports.

5/21

The use of unnecessary massiveness in support structures, particularly in piers and abutments, is overdone. A line of slender single column supports for a two-lane viaduct structure, for example, is far more appropriate than solid masonry piers, as is the general use of small "stub" abutments at the top of a side slope to terminate a bridge crossing.

5/22

New materials and techniques of construction must be constantly explored and applied. The economic and esthetic implications of our modern structural materials—high-strength steels, reinforced concrete, prestressed concrete, aluminum alloys, laminated timbers, stainless steels, plastics, and composites—have not been fully realized in practice.

5/23

The judicious use of color should not be overlooked on bridge structures. A great improvement in the visual quality of our bridges and the other freeway structures and appurtenances of our nation may be achieved by the simple device of painting the steel in attractive solid colors. The aluminum paint so commonly seen is disturbingly reflective when new, and dull when weathered. Bright greens clash with the color of foliage. Pastel shades are not suited to heavy construction. But the primary colors—red, yellow, and blue—seem well suited in the deeper ranges, as do red-browns, tans, olive, and charcoal gray. It is proposed that one color or simple color combination be applied to a significant and unified section of the freeway system.

All colors should be selected and coordinated by an expert in color as well as in the weathering qualities of the various surface applications. Self-coating steels and anodized finishes are promising—as is the use of selected and exposed aggregates in concrete.

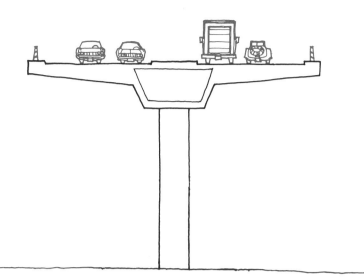

A continuous closed steel box girder with an orthotropic deck plate supported on transverse cantilevers is probably the trimmest elevated road structure.

5/24

Bridge details should be as simple as possible. This statement applies to railings, pylons, guardrails, bearings, and similar elements. Where nearby freestanding sign standards can be eliminated by incorporating the sign within the bridge structure, this should be encouraged. Sign supports and light standards should be detailed to be consistent with bridge details. New concepts of bridge roadway lighting include the use of lighting integral with bridge handrails, which eliminates the need for overhead stanchions. The use of high-intensity area floodlighting on masts such as has been developed for parking fields, offers possibilities for simpler and more favorable illumination of interchanges and wide freeways.

5/25

Highway structures should reveal that the designer has made a careful study of each individual problem. Many bridge details detrimental to the appearance of the structure are the result of an over-literal adherence to specifications or standards of regulatory bodies, and alternates should be developed where possible.

End pylons disproportionate in size, which break the smooth flow of the bridge ribbon, should be avoided.

Exposed stiffeners on the fascia girders of steel bridges, where these are not essential, should be avoided by placing them on the inside (unexposed) face of the girder.

Slavish repetition of curved "butterfly" or T-shaped concrete piers, which are not as handsome as solid pier shafts with straight ends tapered in toward the bottom, should be avoided.

The use of overpass throughway bridges with vertical piers at side shoulders or in the center mall is a weary and dangerous standardization, when the alternates of graceful inclined strut frames and of long-span girders are available to eliminate these hazards.

The continued use of straight, broken-chord fascia beams on curved steel bridges is unnecessary since more pleasing curved fascias can be readily fabricated.

Greater use should be made of wide box-girders in steel, which can achieve the same esthetic grace as has been attained in concrete, and which blend well with the substructure of piers and single columns.

The failure to introduce prestress by tendons or externally induced constraints, in order to "slenderize" steel structures in the same manner as has been done so effectively with those of concrete, has penalized the development of more graceful steel bridges.

5/26

Good bridges are designed with minimal maintenance in mind, but accessibility should be provided for unavoidable maintenance. Corrosion-resistant steel can be used to reduce the need for painting. New steels are available which themselves form an attractive, colorful protective coating, eliminating the need for painting entirely. Concrete should receive protective treatments at the time of construction.

One of the most damaging and destructive factors affecting the appearance of a bridge is the continued use of de-icing salts and chemicals. Major research in evolving better means of solving the icing problems should be continued. The literature in support of this recommendation is voluminous.

5/27

Old, abandoned, or replaced highway structures such as bridge abutments, pavements, culverts, signs, and fences should be removed and the area filled, planted, or seeded to restore it to its former natural state. If not removed promptly, such remnants eventually become eyesores.

5/28

The guidelines enunciated for bridge structures apply in general also to other appurtenant freeway structures. These include retaining walls, culverts and headwalls, and drainage structures.

5/29

The tops of retaining walls should not constitute merely a series of short tangents between different design heights. The top should be smoothed out with long swinging curves to match the natural roll of the country.

5/30

Drainage structures should be as inconspicuous as possible. Culvert end sections should be used in place of concrete headwalls wherever practical. Where slopes are flat the use of flared end sections is preferable since they may be better adjusted to the slope, have improved hydraulic characteristics, are less hazardous to vehicles, more economical, and easier to maintain. Flush grate inlets should be used in medians and roadsides. Down drains should be buried.

5/31

The fewer the signs, the greater the impact of the ones remaining. Wherever practicable they should be incorporated with other structures. Where back to back freestanding signs cannot be used to avoid duplication, the standard and blank back should be painted to blend with the landscape, thus causing the motorist less distraction.

5/32

Bridge railings should be designed in height, material, and section to provide maximum visibility for travelers on the bridge. The views of many of our nation's most spectacular land and water crossings are denied the traveler simply because these views were never considered in the design of the bridge railings.

A bridge rail should be as open in section as possible to provide maximum viewing. It is essential, at the same time, that the bridge edge provide a sense of structural safety and containment.

5/33

The lighting of urban freeways should be considered in terms of the sequential experience of driving. Particular pains should be taken at on-ramp and off-ramp connections and other areas of possible traffic conflict or motorist indecision. The elimination of overhead lighting standards on bridges can be achieved by horizontal lighting of the bridge floor from continuous tube lighting incorporated in the bridge railing. The need for continuous freeway lighting and for the rows of lighting standards required should be reviewed on the basis of overall safety and driving comfort and awareness.

Open tunnels compare favorably in cost with those which are fully enclosed. The advantages are natural lighting and ventilation.

5/34

Shallow tunnels may be opened above for natural lighting at little, if any, additional cost. An open tunnel section roofed by cantilevers or by thin cross girders provides light and ventilation to the vehicle users, while minimizing freeway intrusion on the community traversed and accommodating frequent on-grade crossings.

5/35

Tunnel entrances should be shielded from the sun. The temporary loss of vision upon entering or leaving a tunnel can be diminished by care in location and design. Orientation of the tunnel entrance away from low sun arc is a factor.

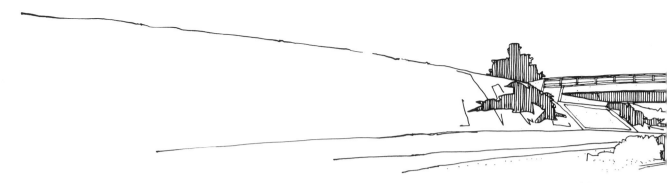

Glare from tunnel portals may be minimized by coloring concrete dark and by judicious use of planting. Devices that gradually increase shielding as the tunnel is approached, and gradually increase lighting as the exit is approached, are needed. Compatible lighting intensity from inside to out could be modulated throughout the day by rheostatic controls.

5/36

The use of tunnels in dense urban areas should be fully explored as a means of preserving parks, historical sites, and landmarks. Tunnels need not be long unrelieved subsurface tubes. They can be designed with openings, widenings, natural lighting, color, and texture to improve the driving experience.

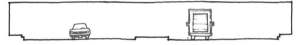

Low, dark two-way tunnels are obsolete.

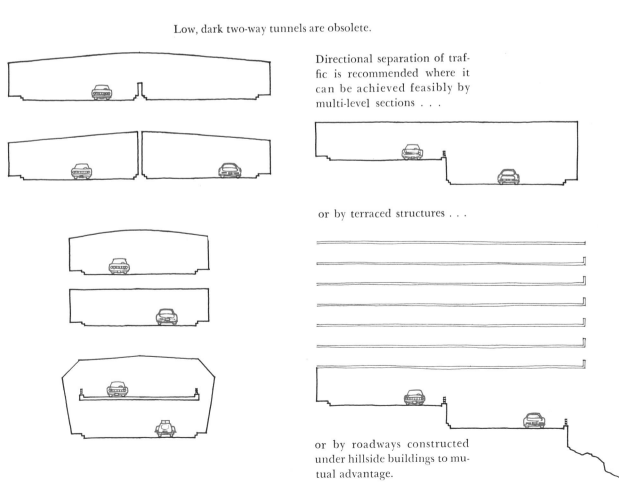

Directional separation of traffic is recommended where it can be achieved feasibly by multi-level sections . . .

or by terraced structures . . .

or by roadways constructed under hillside buildings to mutual advantage.

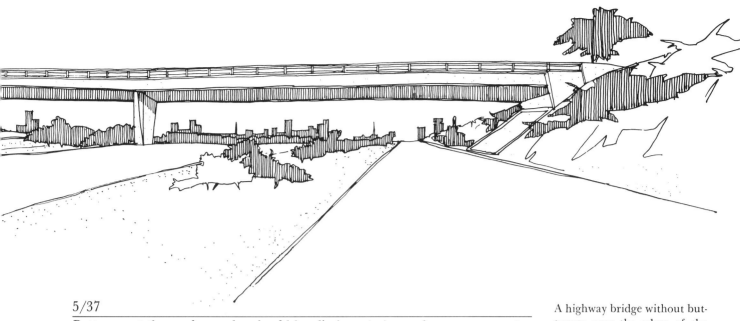

5/37

Buttresses at the roadway edge should be eliminated. As a safety measure and to improve the visual characteristics of the highway wherever feasible, bridges should span the entire width of the roadway, including shoulders.

A highway bridge without buttresses near the edges of the road is both safer and better looking than the bulkier, buttressed type.

5/38

Intermediate piers should be eliminated at medians. The improved appearance and safety of overpasses which cross an expressway by means of a single span (thus completely eliminating intermediate piers in the median and at shoulders) more than outweigh the increase in cost, which is generally on the order of 5 percent of the total cost of the bridges.

The elimination of intermediate piers, and the reduction of piers at the roadway shoulders, provide improved appearance and safety at little additional cost.

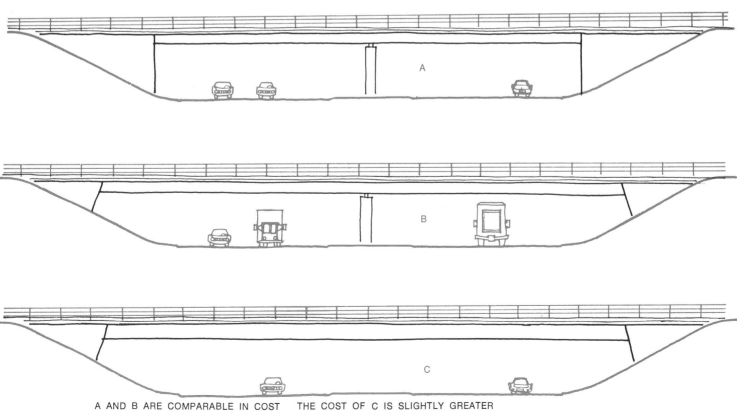

A AND B ARE COMPARABLE IN COST   THE COST OF C IS SLIGHTLY GREATER

6

Multiple
use
of
the
corridor

Out of all serious dialogue on urban expressways today emerges one insistent and compelling idea: that of using the highway to structure or restructure the city. This concept involves multiple use of the highway corridor both vertically and horizontally—the space above and below the road, as well as the space alongside it—in such a way that all of it, the entire corridor, is planned and shaped as an integrated whole.

It is a dramatic concept of a magnitude to match the drama of the problem. Basic to the situation is the critical and growing scarcity of urban land. Economists and planners, concerned with proper and controlled land use, are naturally alarmed when they see increasing areas of tax-producing real estate set aside for exclusive highway purposes.

The use of air rights over railroads is a well established custom in this country. Now we are beginning to see apartment houses, hotels, and restaurants built over highways, too. Highways and urban renewal projects have been developed cooperatively in many states, including New York and California. Some internal freeways have been deliberately located through the worst slums to help the city in its program of slum clearance and urban renewal.

The federal government has greeted the concept with enthusiasm. the Bureau of Public Roads has declared itself "ready to work with the nation's cities—to seek new and bold uses of the joint development concept to achieve maximum use of that part of our scarce urban land which must be devoted to highway transportation." In making its offer, BPR takes care to address itself to the sensitive political-social problems of the displacement of people and removal of scarce intercity land areas from tax rolls. It points out that in heavily built-up residential areas, apartments

81

can replace row housing in about one-third of the space formerly used. When this happens the other two-thirds can be devoted to other kinds of development, and careful coordination can assure that "new replacement housing would be available for those displaced, as construction progresses."

Such a program could be financed in a variety of ways, but all of its supporters see economics as the key to its success. One attractive feature is that in areas of greatest need, the land required for blockwide multiple use can be acquired for little more than the cost of land for freeway use alone. A city could acquire entire blocks on the route of a planned freeway, which it could buy for not much more than the highway department would have to spend (considering severance damages as well as right-of-way costs) for just the portion of the block needed. The city would then sell to the highway department the space needed for the freeway, at the same right-of-way plus severance damage price which the department would have had to pay. The cost of the highway thus would be no less

Market East development scheme proposed for Philadelphia

and no more, but the city would acquire the adjoining land very cheaply for its other facilities.

Some experts would go further and give the highway department itself the authority to condemn and purchase the area immediately adjoining a proposed freeway or interchange. It could then sell the unused "improved land" (for the presence of the highway would greatly enhance its value) for private or public development projects.

Either method would work to the advantage of the community; for the cost factor of highway construction becomes less critical when revenue is produced by subsidiary uses of the corridor. This is the strength of the concept—its benefit to the highway department in terms of more peaceable land acquisition and its benefit to the city in terms of better traffic access, possibilities of renewal on a more significant and creative scale, the removal of less land from the tax rolls, and for all concerned the reduced long-range cost of freeway construction. The highway would no longer be the intruder. It would be a welcome component of the new city structure—as much a part of its architecture as a fine building.

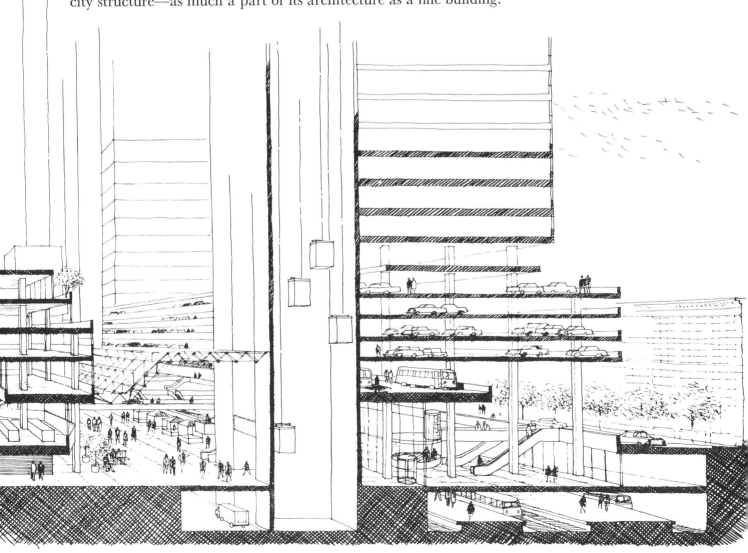

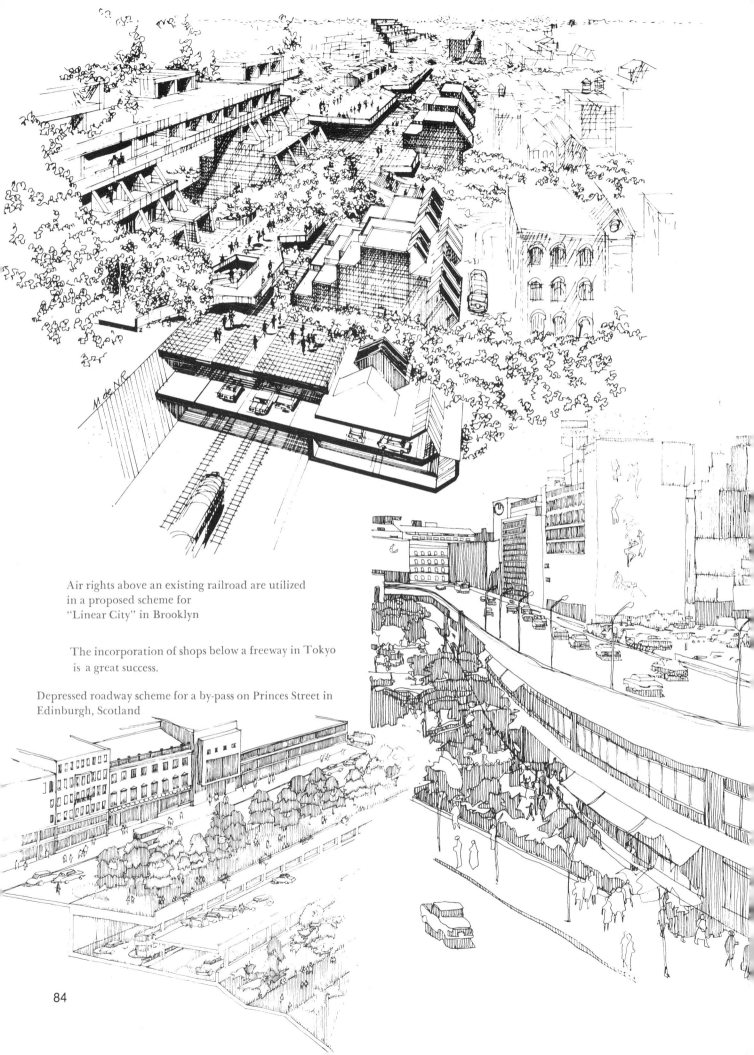

Air rights above an existing railroad are utilized
in a proposed scheme for
"Linear City" in Brooklyn

The incorporation of shops below a freeway in Tokyo
is a great success.

Depressed roadway scheme for a by-pass on Princes Street in
Edinburgh, Scotland

84

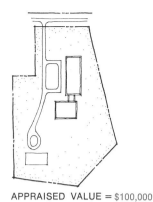

APPRAISED VALUE = $100,000

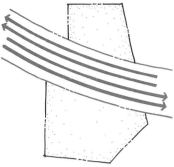

RIGHT-OF-WAY AND
SEPARATION COSTS = $140,000

6/1

Maximum multiple utilization of urban expressway rights-of-way should be explored and developed. Such use must be in conformity with comprehensive regional planning and established business and living patterns, and should be logically related to the three-dimensional forms of both the city and the highway itself. Criteria for such multiple use should be established as a result of team study for each facility built.

The Department of Transportation might well join with the Department of Housing and Urban Development in a series of major study projects demonstrating the possibilities of imaginative multiple use of urban freeway corridors. This research effort should aim at the development of new procedures, financial aid programs,and enabling legislation.

Present legislation normally prescribes a fixed right-of-way width for highways of various categories. But if the total parcel of affected land could be acquired by the highway department at the appraised value (plus equitable replacement and moving costs) the cost of the property would often be less than for partial acquisition. The excess land could then either be developed for highway-related uses or sold or leased for other purposes.

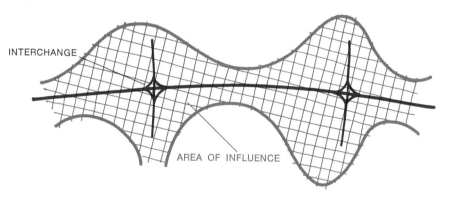

INTERCHANGE

AREA OF INFLUENCE

The appreciated value of property near freeway interchanges — resulting solely from the presence, or proposed location of a new highway — should revert to the state. If this land were to be purchased with highway acquisition funds and resold or leased to developers as *improved land,* the proceeds would help to underwrite a substantial part of the total highway program.

6/2

Private improvements should be permitted and encouraged on highway rights-of-way. The probability of private capital's being unable to carry the burden of the entire extra cost of development over or under the highway should be recognized. Since such development recoups for the city or metropolitan region valuable space, and since it requires abnormal cost in terms of capital outlay and planning coordination, it is proposed that it be encouraged by grants of local, state, and federal aid. Just as urban redevelopment is subsidized, so should the multiple use of the highway corridors be subsidized. Just as redevelopment projects involving private investment are taxable—so should comparable projects entailing multiple use be taxable also.

6/3

Both public agencies and private entrepreneurs should be given guidance and help in multiple use planning. Present deterrents include lack of information, complications in the staging of design and construction, and the fear of red tape and delays. Government publications are needed to inform potential developers of the opportunities, benefits, and incentives which exist or are brought into being. Information is also needed on the step by step joint planning procedures required. These should be streamlined and the review process and project staging in all ways expedited.

6/4

A rapid extension of the multiple-use concept is an absolute essential if freeways are to be built in high-density urban areas in the future. When the freeway, through its multiple-use and air-rights possibilities, adds to, rather than subtracts from, the store of buildable urban space, and augments, rather than decreases, the tax ratables, it will have greatly enhanced its position in the city—and its welcome.

6/5

New air-rights legislation and techniques must be developed and applied. An investigation into the uses of freeway air rights over expressways has only begun but the possibilities hold great promise. These include:

The expanded use of public or private parking and recreation facilities under or alongside elevated highway structures, or on decks or plazas above the roadway.

The construction of complexes that include residential or office space and related parking decks and plazas, plus the highway, in the form of a three-dimensional "air tunnel."

Freeways that move through the city atop, through, or across commercial, institutional, light industrial, or residential structures, using air rights purchased or leased from the basic landowner.

The right of airspace use to be conveyed by purchase, lease, or by easements, alone or in combination.

6/6

Space below elevated highway structures should be planned for present or future commercial, light industrial, parking, or other use, public or private. This entails a reasonably long column spacing to provide flexibility for varied uses. Public officials and owners of adjacent property and businesses should be encouraged to use this space under reasonably restrictive arrangements common in commercial lease arrangements.

6/7

Highway planning should be related to urban renewal. By coordinating the two programs, the cities will have an opportunity to rebuild into something truly great. New legislation providing the right of excess condemnation will permit entire city blocks to be restructured into an integrated fusion of highway, park, housing, and commercial building.

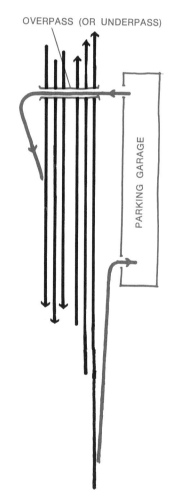

OVERPASS (OR UNDERPASS)

PARKING GARAGE

Where major parking facilities are placed beside or over urban freeways, direct access should be provided, rather than forcing drivers to move needlessly through the city streets. Generous ramp length is required to avoid traffic backup.

Possibilities of roadway placement within the multi-use corridor

Roadway at grade

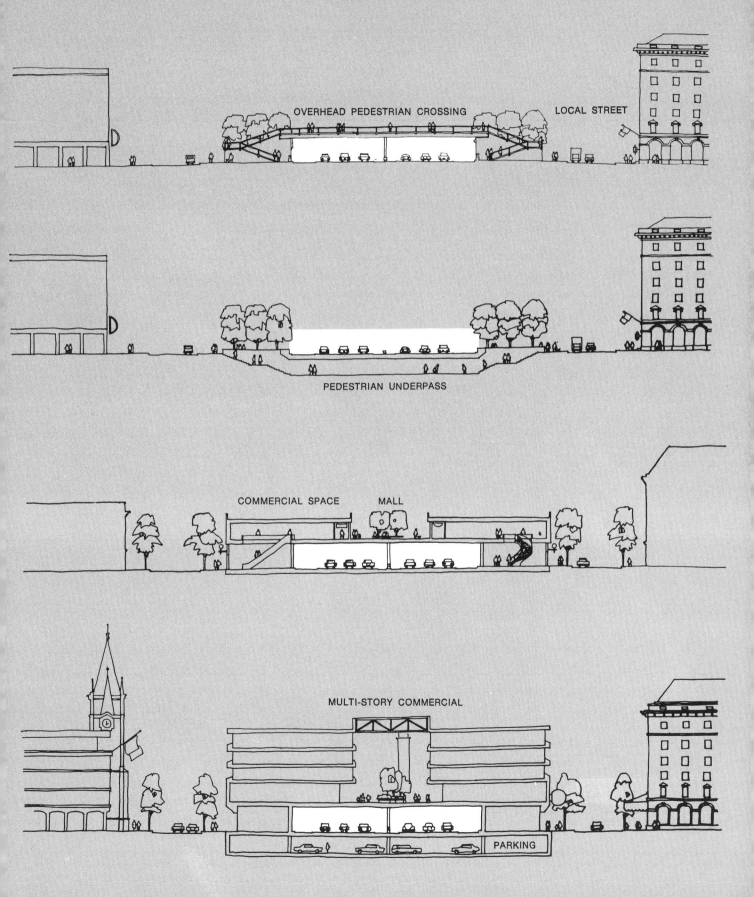

OVERHEAD PEDESTRIAN CROSSING   LOCAL STREET

PEDESTRIAN UNDERPASS

COMMERCIAL SPACE   MALL

MULTI-STORY COMMERCIAL

PARKING

Depressed roadway

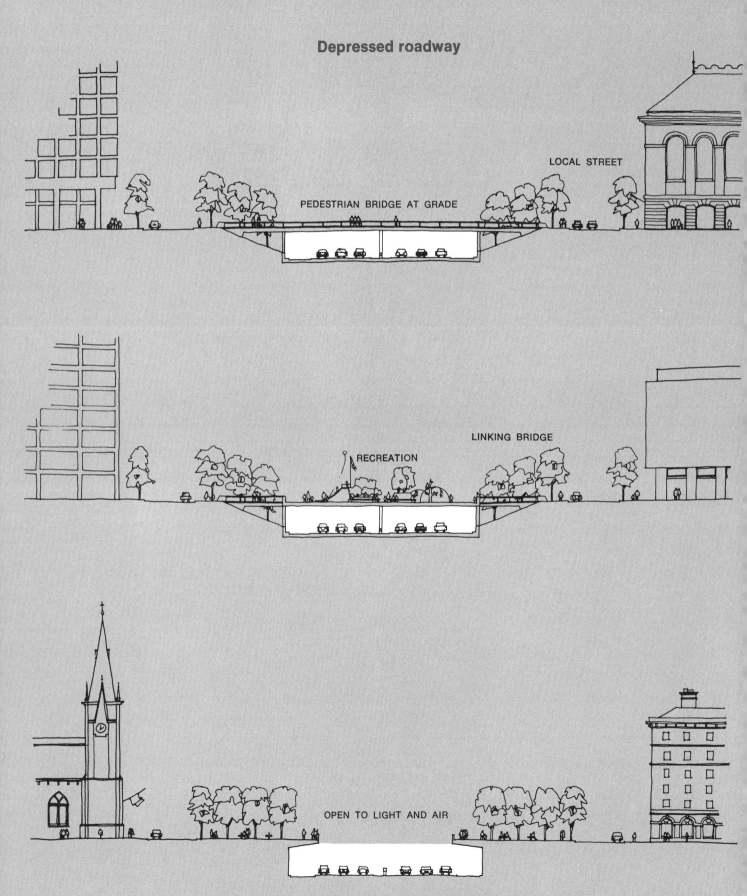

LOCAL STREET

PEDESTRIAN BRIDGE AT GRADE

LINKING BRIDGE

RECREATION

OPEN TO LIGHT AND AIR

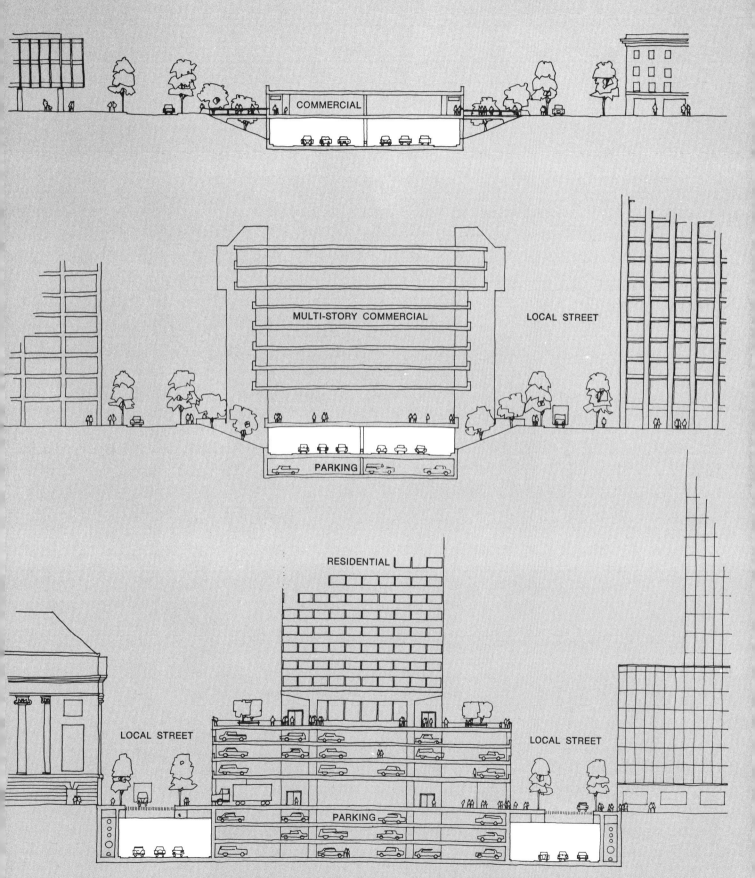

COMMERCIAL

MULTI-STORY COMMERCIAL   LOCAL STREET

PARKING

RESIDENTIAL

LOCAL STREET   LOCAL STREET

PARKING

Elevated roadway

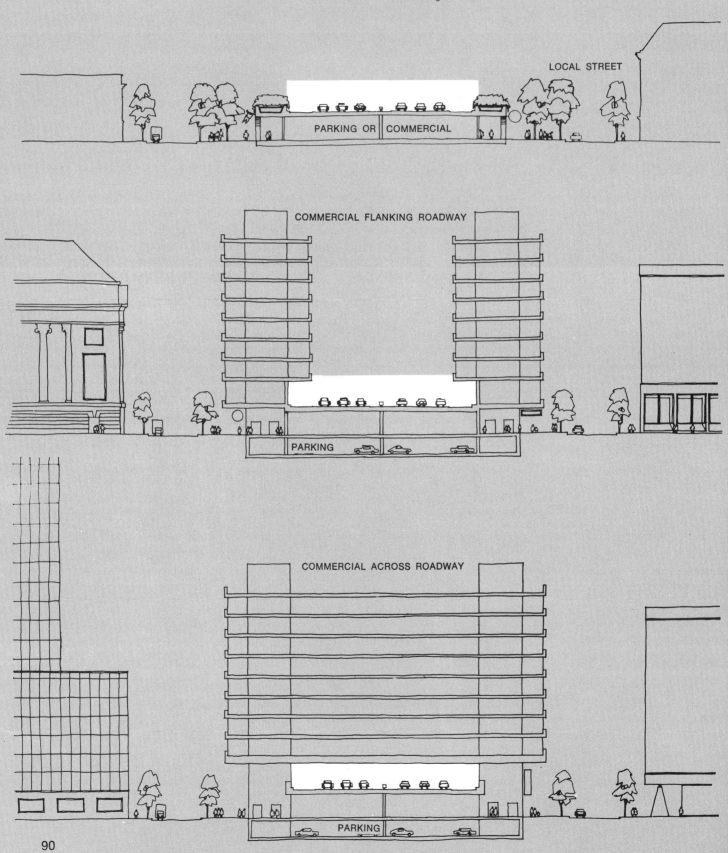

LOCAL STREET

PARKING OR | COMMERCIAL

COMMERCIAL FLANKING ROADWAY

PARKING

COMMERCIAL ACROSS ROADWAY

PARKING

Decked roadway

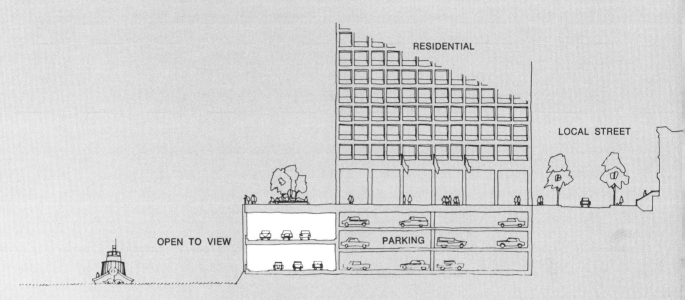

RESIDENTIAL

LOCAL STREET

OPEN TO VIEW

PARKING

Terraced roadway

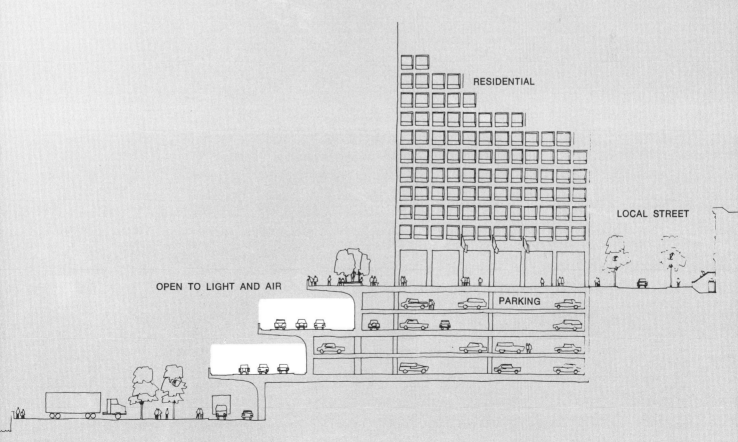

RESIDENTIAL

LOCAL STREET

OPEN TO LIGHT AND AIR

PARKING

6/8

A combined traffic-transportation-transit right-of-way has many benefits. It is time for the cities to consider the acquisition of broad 500- to 1,000-foot open space bands which could be leased for highway transit and other compatible transportation development. Perhaps only thus can the normal disruption of freeway construction be prevented. And perhaps only thus may future and as yet unimagined traffic systems be accommodated. Such city owned and leased bands may provide space for pneumatic tubes for transit and transportation, air rights for the many related uses served, or routes for free-flight bubbles.

6/9

Highway departments should be encouraged to purchase and develop freeway-recreation corridors. Freeways should not only provide access to but should be considered in themselves as major recreation facilities. A bold approach is envisioned by which the freeway is designed to move through an expanded right-of-way purchased by the highway departments in concert with municipalities, and devoted to scenic and recreational purposes.

Existing areas of outstanding natural or man-made scenic beauty could be bypassed and their quality preserved by stringent zoning regulations, rather than by outright purchase. Proposed freeway-recreation corridors could well be located through lands of low-grade productivity or low scenic quality—such as stripped areas, spoil piles, or dumps. A new landscape of reforested hills and waterways embracing recreation features could be developed by the application of landscape design principles.

6/10

In the meantime, a common right-of-way provides obvious benefits of location, land taking, and joint construction. There are, however, inherent drawbacks to this arrangement which must be recognized and overcome. Provision must be made for vehicular and pedestrian crossings of the additional right-of-way width, in particular, to gain access to the transit stations. A public transit route usually best serves a narrow and high-density residential band which depends upon public transit rather than the automobile for primary transportation. The introduction of freeways through this band, side by side with transit ways, brings high-speed automobile traffic through a non-automobile-oriented community. But in some cases conditions of topography or community structure eliminate the detrimental effects.

6/11

The freeway right-of-way should be expanded laterally to include that strip of highway-related land the value of which is most directly appreciated by freeway presence. With new enabling legislation, this freeway-improved, freeway-appreciated, freeway-related land might well provide the base for a wide range of multiple uses which could do much to defray the roadway construction costs.

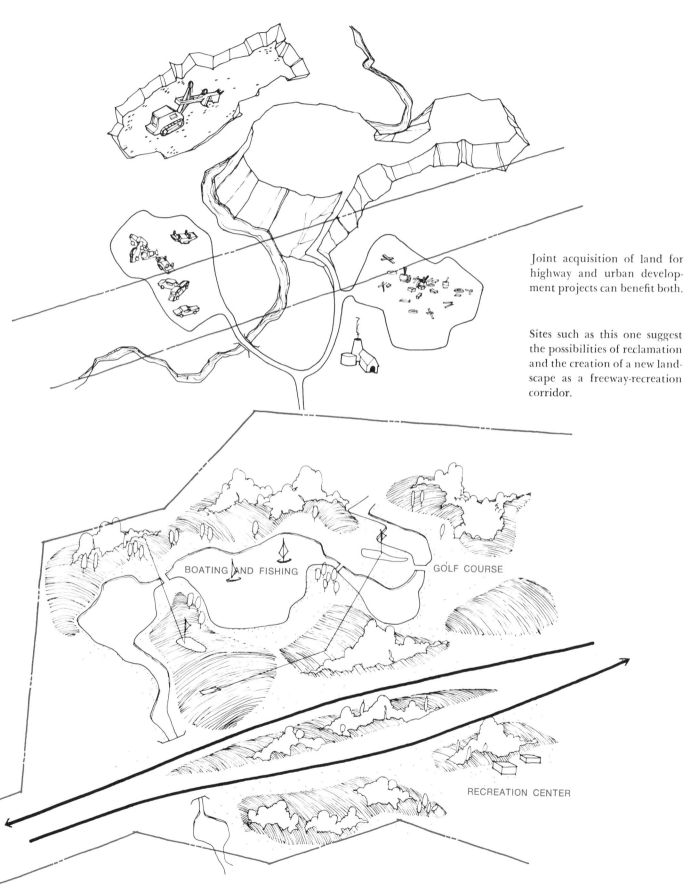

Joint acquisition of land for highway and urban development projects can benefit both.

Sites such as this one suggest the possibilities of reclamation and the creation of a new landscape as a freeway-recreation corridor.

BOATING AND FISHING

GOLF COURSE

RECREATION CENTER

In even the most densely populated American city, ingenuity and effort in design can make roadways conform to natural and cultural contours. Two roadways in our largest metropolis prove the point: Manhattan's Franklin D. Roosevelt Drive and the Brooklyn-Queens Connecting Highway at Columbia Heights, shown on the succeeding pages.

The East River
(Franklin Delano Roosevelt)
Drive

Thousands of motorists move uptown and downtown daily beside the boat traffic which plies the East River in New York City. The freeway is the Franklin D. Roosevelt Drive, where for scores of blocks traffic is freed from stop and go lights.

Yet the FDR Drive does not divorce the city from the river, as some freeways do. The roadway changes character from section to section along much of its length just as the city does, in order to accommodate, sometimes even improve, the sites of apartment houses, hospitals, and other institutions (including the United Nations headquarters), individual homes, and commercial and industrial structures which line its corridor. Pedestrian overpasses provide direct access to the waterside.

On the next two pages is a particularly telling photograph of how this expressway, over the years, has been woven into the fabric of a city.

Right, from the air, is the United Nations group. Here the FDR Drive becomes virtually a tunnel— but a tunnel with continuous windows on the river. Above the roadway UN offices and restaurants overhang to the river's edge, as does also the peaceful rose garden.

Below is a view of the FDR Drive straight on from the East River. North and South traffic are separated vertically in this section, at the foot of cliffs of apartment houses with one of the world's most highly prized—and highest priced—views.

Right: on the FDR Drive, is a narrow and rather barren park—except for its immense river view. It is accessible by the stairway down from the broad deck which roofs the upper roadway.

Below is a stretch of the FDR Drive where it passes beside New York Hospital. The slim park along the river edge can be reached by pedestrian overpasses.

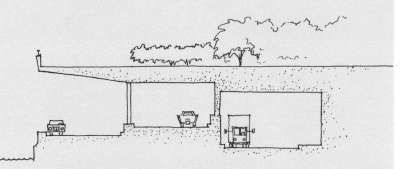

Diagram of the FDR Drive treatment at the UN reveals the stepped levels of the uptown and downtown roadways, retaining the river view for passengers in both directions. A service road makes for easy access to the UN's garages. The ramped road in the photograph below is an access for uptown traffic.

Brooklyn-Queens
Connecting Highway
at
Columbia Heights

The problem here was how to install a capacious freeway beside docking facilities at the foot of a steep hill overlooking New York Harbor. The site was a choice one, in Brooklyn Heights, south of the old Brooklyn Bridge. At the top of the hill were apartments and beautiful old houses whose backyards had views only begun to be described by the photograph right. At the bottom, a local road.

The design solution: dig back into the hill a few feet, build a rugged stepped retaining wall, and cantilever two three-lane roadways from it. The local street underneath was undisturbed; so were the houses on the top. Best of all, a third "roadway" was added on the top level behind the houses and turned into a public park and promenade, one of New York's finest manmade places. Overleaf is evidence.

It is possible that more of the principles outlined in this report have been applied to the Brooklyn-Queens Connecting Highway than to any other single urban freeway. If the result seems less like highway construction than sensitive urban achitecture, this is a sure mark of its success.

Serving as a buffer between the riverside wharves and the residential district above, the multi-level expressway improves the functions and prospects of both. In diverting through traffic from the already crowded local streets, the Brooklyn-Queens Expressway ameliorated existing problems, precluded others, and provided a genuine addition to the community.

No extra land in addition to the freeway right-of-way had to be bought to create the promenade in Brooklyn—and the right-of-way for the freeway itself is only 50 feet wider than the old street over which the entire structure is set.

Below is an entrance from the dense local street pattern to the park, with its view across the water to the Wall Street section of Manhattan. Part of this residential area, Brooklyn Heights, has been designated a Historical Preservation District—and this includes the freeway structure.

Right is shown one end of the promenade and the steel which supports it. Below is a view of the entire structure from one of the ships warehouse roofs. Note the relatively open guard rails on the roadways, which do not block the sweeping view from riders, and the concealed overhead lighting sources, equally unobtrusive.

7
The systems approach

Current freeway planning procedures have not met fully the measure of the problems or the possibilities of urban transportation. For the most part highway planners have instead followed, and extended by logic, those methods which have successfully solved the problems of rural freeway construction.

But as the highway sweeps toward and into metropolitan areas, problems confronted are not the same. Needs are different; opportunities are different; even values are different. Rural highways have been successful and well received in rural areas because they were devised to meet rural conditions. When urban freeways are planned and designed to respond fully to the needs of the cities and their people, they will be successful. The factors are so diverse that freeways can only be planned in relationship to urban centers by the application of a variety of contemporary technological disciplines collectively described as the "systems approach."

The systems approach is fundamentally a decision-making process. It considers alternative approaches to overall design (or to a problem) to arrive at a system that provides optimum performance with respect to established criteria. The system itself may be an integrated assembly of interacting elements, components, or subsystems, designed to carry out collectively a predetermined function. The systems approach is best suited to dynamic problems, where conditions of load, capacity, environment, or other information inputs vary with time.

This process has been successfully applied by the federal government, its agencies, and consultants to such complex problems as military logistics, missile development, and the space program. It has provided many branches of government, business and industry, and "pure science" with a sophisticated tool for determining aims, analyzing alternatives, and reaching decisions. All these characteristics indicate that the systems approach has become not only useful but essential to urban highway planning. The 1962 highway act, administered by the Federal Highway Administration, requires a "cooperative, comprehensive, and continuing" transportation planning process. For this, the systems approach is ideally suited.

It must be noted, however, that systems analysis is in no sense a method of design; it is rather a process leading up to design, a technique for assuring that the design will be based on a consideration of all the factors bearing on a given problem. In the final analysis nothing of great quality or beauty can be achieved without the efforts of fine intuitive designers.

The systems approach evolved as a rigorous method for handling complex planning problems that required, first, a clear expression of the combinations of forces, equipment, projects, and strategy needed to achieve a particular objective; and, second, a precise organizing, scheduling, and evaluating of the components once a selection has been made. The method responsive to the first need was referred to as SYSTEMS ANALYSIS, because each of the possibilities is frequently considered as a "system" combining all the elements—men, machines, and strategy—needed to gain the objective. For a similar reason, the method responsive to the second need was referred to as SYSTEMS ENGINEERING.

A system may be described as any set of objects with relationship between the objects and between their attributes. Thus, systems can consist of highways, bridges, communities, equations, laws, or processes. ATTRIBUTES are properties of objects; highways, for example, have length and width. RELATIONSHIPS tie systems together, and may be logical, casual or random. Any system functions within the influence of its ENVIRONMENT, which is composed of those objects or factors lying outside the system which have a significant effect upon it. The five environmental factors which affect man-made systems are:

1. the state of technology
2. the natural environment (climate, plant life, ecological processes, etc.)
3. organizational policies
4. the economic conditions for new systems
5. human factors

Systems analysis

It is generally conceded that the systems approach is an outgrowth of operations research, which was evolved by the British military in 1939. Since scientists from many fields had contributed to the development of weapons, radar, and other inventions—and since their proper application was dependent upon an understanding of their components and their nature—an interdisciplinary team was assembled to devise methods of optimum use. The results were so satisfactory that the application of scientific method by a team of experts to the performance of elements within whole systems became an established procedure in Great Britain. Operations research teams were called in when there was a problem that required highly technical knowledge for its solution. When these successes were reported to the United States the Armed Forces were soon employing the "OR" approach to a wide variety of problems which had proved too complex for traditional procedures. As the defense operations of World War II grew more intensively scientific, scientists and the scientific method became an integral part of government.

"So", *Progressive Architecture* magazine has reported, "the stage was set for the postwar development of systems analysis and operations research in many fields—civilian and space age as well as military. The basic concept of expert teamwork, scientific method, and sequential treatment of all parameters of a problem was found to be ideally amenable to evolution through more sophisticated concepts of research and investigative methods (computers, information retrieval devices, and so on). Today, there would seem to be few areas of planning or research immune to the potentials of systems analysis and problem solving, imaginatively pursued and constructively used."

The analysis of systems and their environments as employed in systems analysis and in the closely related area of operations research is essentially the study of anything as part of a larger process or system. It is the consideration of all segments as tied together by interdependent functions.

Systems analysis is further characterized by the following conditions:

1. the scientific method is always followed

2. the work is usually done according to a prescribed formula or sequence of jobs

3. an interdisciplinary team rather than an individual performs the work

Though exceptions and variations sometimes do occur, depending on the nature of the problem being studied, it is fair to say that, if the characteristics listed are not present, systems analysis is not being performed.

The scientific method, applied in both systems analysis and operations research involves three steps:

1. The formulation of a theory to account for a set of isolated facts, or observations of the environment;

2. Checking to see whether the theory actually explains the known facts, which involves formulating and reformulating (and reformulating again) the facts in terms of theory;

3. Testing the theory's validity by seeing whether or not it accurately predicts events (i.e. gives the correct result).

Formulation of theory

In systems analysis the theory is called the model of the problem, process, or system, and the setting up of the theory (or model) is known as simulation. The model may be the mathematical, or sometimes physical or analog, representation of the facts and behavior of whole systems—engineering, architectural, industrial, social, historical, economic, political, or otherwise. By manipulating the equations or values of the model, alternative means can be evaluated to test the effect of certain actions on results or goals. A general form of mathematical models may be expressed by the formula $E = f(X_i, Y_j)$ in which E, the effect of any system on the environment or performance, is a result of the interaction of X_i, the independent variables, and Y_j, the dependent variables. In practice, symbols in this model are replaced with numbers describing the actual system and its environment.

Figure 1 illustrates a block diagram of typical steps in the systems approach to a planning problem. Goals and objectives are frequently very difficult to state, and may in fact be multiple and conflicting in character. Constraints define the physical, financial, timing, risk, policy, and other considerations which the plan or design must satisfy. The search for alternatives encourages innovation and creativity and the avoidance of prejudgment, in a process popularly called "brainstorming." Feedback is the continual process of reviewing and modifying prior steps in the light of decisions reached at each stage of the progess. Optimization is the process of continual adjustment of a systems model until the best set of conditions is obtained.

Systems analysis has been termed a "horizontal approach" because it reaches out in contrast with the "vertical" or departmental approach, which reaches up or down.

While a departmental approach has certain acknowledged strengths it has also obvious shortcomings. To reach the problem solver, information and expert opinion must flow up or down the ladder of responsibility, each transfer subjecting the data or suggestion to review and often modification or veto. Creative suggestions are too often rejected or never reach the

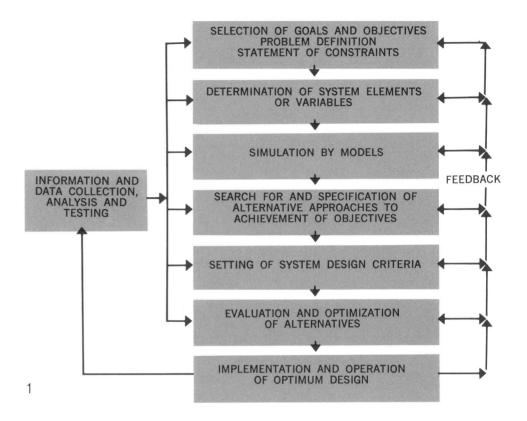

decision-maker; or expert opinion is modified on the basis of another point of view. Often within a given department there are men who could contribute essential knowledge or a fresh point of view to a problem under consideration; but for reasons inherent in any departmental organization, they are never heard from.

Systems analysis differs from the departmental approach in several significant respects. An essential feature of the systems approach is that it assembles a team of experts on the same level of authority who may discuss, and argue, all aspects of a problem freely in the presence of the person or persons who will make the decision. The decision-makers are thereby exposed to maximum intercommunication, and to an uninhibited exploration of the full range of factors bearing on the problem in question. Quantifiable data are presented as fact. Data which are non-quantifiable (in terms of present capabilities) such as social, historical, political, or esthetic values are discussed by men who are knowledgeable in these fields.

Given the same body of experts, it is proposed that their effectiveness would be greater in the systems context and approach than if they were made to operate within and through a departmental structure.

In simplest terms the systems approach involves the following general steps:

1. PROBLEM DEFINITION. The specific problem to be studied is defined in detail by the project leader. It is described in its full and proper context and lists primary and secondary considerations.

2. TEAM ASSEMBLY. In light of the problem definition, a team of experts is assembled. Together, they should be knowledgeable in the various fields involved. They may serve the team full time, or appear as requested, during the period of study. It is important that the team members be advised from the start in whose hands the final decision-making will lie—in the full team, a subcommittee, the study director, or a separate group. It is also important that those responsible for the decision be present at all discussion conferences.

3. DEVELOPMENT OF STUDY PROCEDURES. Much thought is given to the best means of attacking the main problem and its subsidiary problems. This normally leads to the formulation of mathematical, graphic, physical, or analog models. It is essential that means be devised by which, as the study progresses, information is gathered and processed and assumptions or conclusions tested and found to be correct or false—that there is constant feedback or readjustment of the models and input data.

4. INVESTIGATION AND ANALYSIS. The team must be provided with adequate means of investigation and analysis. Here on-site investigation, three-dimensional models, visual aids, comprehensive planning procedures, and the use of computer techniques are among the possibilities. The aim is to insure that the team and its decision unit become aware of all pertinent factors and information.

5. DECISION-MAKING. Once the decision unit has been exposed to all discussion and data that it feels to be necessary the team is dismissed, or perhaps left on call, and a judgment on the best feasible solution is then reached and reported.

6. IMPLEMENTATION. Often the team investigation and discussions include exploration not only of a proposed solution but also of the means by which it can be carried forward. Or it may fall to the decision-maker to plan and describe such measures. In either event it is clear that no proposals can be any better than the mechanism or means by which they are to be implemented.

System components

In urban highway planning it is not sufficient to set as a goal the most efficient method of connecting point A with point B. The primary purpose must be to produce a fine community in which the freeway functions as an integral part; a community in which people live, work, and pursue happiness with maximum amenity, and in which services and safety are achieved at reasonable cost. To this end transportation planning can only be reasonably carried forward as an integrated aspect of total urban and regional planning. This process encompasses simulation models which intermesh urban activities, tripmaking, model choice, and traffic assignment. It employs a multidisciplinary staff and committee structure, providing the forum for the enunciation of community goals and objectives and rendering value judgment decisions on regionwide transportation networks and corridors. It is proposed that in addition to corridor network studies, the systems approach should be applied to specific cases of difficult or controversial project planning, or the location and preliminary design of sections of urban highways.

In the systems approach to the urban highway planning process there are a number of components or subsystems to be considered.

The Federal Highway Administration-Bureau of Public Roads Control memoranda issued to implement the broad planning requirements of the Federal-Aid Highway Act of 1962 establish as the basic elements of areawide correlative planning the following:

1. Economic factors affecting development.
      (These include natural resources, climate, land structure, physiography, geographic location relating to trade routes and resources. Included also are traditions of regional development policy, political organization and controls, customs and social structure.)

2. Population

3. Land use

4. Transportation facilities

5. Travel patterns

6. Terminal and transfer facilities

7. Traffic control features

8. Zoning ordinances and building regulations

9. Financial resources

10. Social and community values

The Urban Mass Transportation Act and the Federal Housing Act each also propose critical elements to be considered. The general commonality of factors has been summarized by C. G. Beer as follows:

DEVELOPING AREA-WIDE OBJECTIVES

Social and community values
Recreation and conservation
Economic factors affecting development
Geography and climate

DETERMINING FUTURE ACTIVITIES

Natural resources
Population and employment
Zoning and building regulations
Land-use plan

DETERMINING ALTERNATIVE TRANSPORT SYSTEMS

Modal assignment (modal split)
Terminals and transfers
Traffic control

TESTING AND REPORTING ALTERNATIVE PLANS

Proposed financing
Plan adoption

Other systems of grouping components can be devised to reflect local needs. The important point is that each systems team, in the consideration of any highway planning problem, must draw up its own checklist of components, each clearly defined. The understanding of the factors affecting each component and their interrelationships is fundamental to systems analysis.

Value methodology

Closely related to the systems approach in the planning and design of urban freeways, and therefore properly included in the same discussion, are developing techniques of rating values.

During the past few years, because of a growing sense of need—and as a consequence of the computer's capacity to manipulate and test the implications of weighted variables—intensified study has been made of value methodology, the means and possibilities of assigning values to both quantifiable and unquantifiable factors.

In urban freeway planning, while other factors have been considered, the conventional cost-benefit analysis of urban freeway systems was designed for the evaluation of alternative plans in terms of a single objective—economic efficiency. Translation into monetary values is difficult, perhaps impossible, for intangible costs and benefits which may, indeed, have a significance for the community comparable to or greater than those which can be expressed in dollar units.

A more sophisticated methodology is therefore necessary to evaluate alternative urban highway systems in terms of their multidimensional objectives, including cultural, political, ethical, esthetic, and technical, as well as economic factors.

Review of published material on methods of evaluating costs and benefits of freeway and other traffic improvements has indicated that while a number of methods are promising, and throw light upon the nature of community needs and environmental objectives, no method has yet been developed to a point where its application in the systems approach has been considered sound. Some of these are based on graphical procedures; others are essentially weighting methods. All methods hinge upon the assumption that the collective value judgments of a community have been, or can be, accurately measured and expressed. This is, of course, shaky ground.

Further research on value methodology should be encouraged both for its indirect benefits and perhaps, in time, its direct application. In the meanwhile, both in the planning of regional transportation systems and in the design of specific planning projects, it is believed that the most effective system of rating all costs and benefits is one which:

Gives accurate mathematical values to all factors or alternatives (such as land acquisition costs, or maintenance costs) to which a cost or benefit can be so assigned.

Quantifies all other attributes (such as families dislocated, taxable land taken, or new land made accessible).

Describes through expert opinion those attributes (social, historic, and esthetic, among others) which can be neither costed nor quantified.

If these factors can be clearly presented to, and freely discussed by, an interdisciplinary team within the systems context, the decision-making process will be the most effective possible within the limits of present technology.

Computer applications

Most new methods of highway location and analysis rely heavily on the use of computers to reduce vast quantities of information to manageable form. In its early application to highway planning the computer was used solely to check the balance of earthwork quantities along a given alignment. Its present applications are far more sophisticated, as may be seen in the following sampling.

THE DIGITAL TERRAIN MODEL SYSTEM

In use for the past five years by a number of state highway departments, this system translates the three-dimensional terrain map of an area into a pattern of digits that can be stored in the computer. It is then possible to

2

3

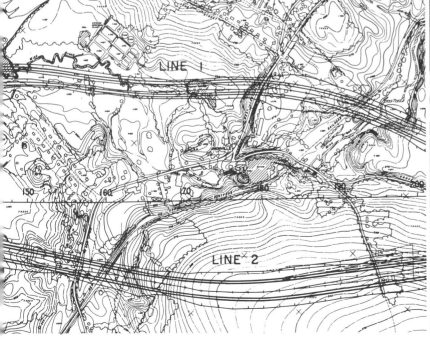

4

analyze rapidly and economically any alternate routes that may be drawn manually through the area. (See figures 2, 3, and 4.)

Given adequate data, the computer compares the effect of each route upon the terrain and produces a summary of all construction and user costs, including the consumption of gas, oil, and tire rubber. It is also possible to calculate costs of land required for right-of-way.

While the foregoing system can only rank alternative routes in order of costs, other researchers are at work on a more comprehensive approach that may in time make feasible the quantification of many social, esthetic, and other nonmonetary benefits as well.

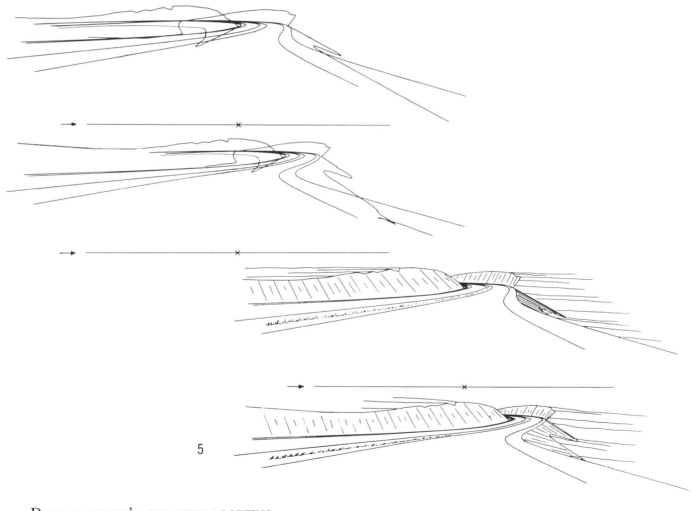

5

DIGITAL DRIVER'S EYE VIEW PLOTTING ⟶

Using a computerized plotting system to produce complete sets of drawings for their highway projects, the French have developed a subroutine which provides perspective drawings of the highway itself from the same data used in the earthworks program. (See figure 5.) This produces a series of "driver's eye views" at successive stations along the proposed highway, each taking a matter of seconds. The views are used to reveal potential hazards which might be the cause of driver error or fatigue. The views at the top are the original machine plottings. While these tracings are readily "read" by the trained eye, those at the bottom have been retouched by a draftsman for committee presentation. The same agency which developed the perspective plottings has produced an animated film of a proposed underground interchange near the Paris Étoile. The film clearly demonstrated the fact that drivers would often overshoot the side exit being tested. With this prior warning the designers were able to make the necessary corrections well in advance of actual construction.

OTHER TECHNIQUES   Several major cities have recently undertaken an extensive program of computer mapping which will record for each parcel of land within the city limits those characteristics which are of most importance to immediate zoning considerations and to long-range planning objectives. Other cities have turned to the computer for the storing, sorting, and plotting of basic planning data.

The importance to urban planning of having current statistical data available is further demonstrated by a map (figure 6) of St. Louis from a

recent urban atlas, which shows a 250-meter-square grid of color-coded symbols overprinted on a U.S. Geodetic Survey of the city. The symbols designate land uses, population characteristics, and income density. Such maps, on a regionwide basis, should be invaluable in highway and transportation planning.

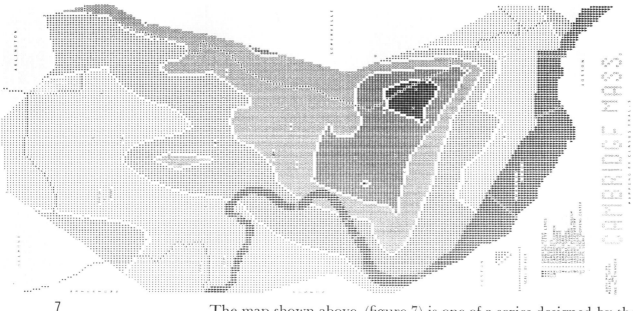

7

The map shown above (figure 7) is one of a series designed by the Harvard Laboratory for Computer Graphics in a study of Cambridge, Mass., the community in which the university is located. "The result of many thousands of calculations, the map was produced on standard equipment at the Harvard Computing Center, in about a minute, from 1960 census data for population and area. The darkest zone indicates the highest 20 percent of the range of the data (58 to 72 persons per acre) while the lightest zone shows the lowest 20 percent (5 to 18 persons per acre) with the three intermediate levels falling in between. The numerals scattered throughout the map are called 'data points' and indicate where data was gathered. When data are collected by zone, in this case census tracts, the data points are located at the zone centers. The number also indicates the density level in which the point occurs. The area of dark triangles shows the Charles River, while the X's indicate bridges. CEM in the lower left designates Cambridge Cemetery and if you look closely you can see other landmark symbols, such as H for Harvard Square, and C for Central Square."

As plotted by computer to show population per acre, the Cambridge map presents a shape quite recognizable to all who are familiar with the city. It could also have been mapped according to family income, average mortgage on dwellings, parcel assessment, religious or racial backgrounds—or according to any other measure of the community or its inhabitants for which data could be made available.

Aside from its use to planners this method of graphically recording complex statistical or other quantitative data has obvious and direct application to urban sociologists and economists and to government agencies concerned with such matters as highway and transportation planning.

The examples given include but a random few of the applications of the digital computer to the freeway planning process. But while systems analysis provides a logical field of operation for the computer, the use of a computer is not essential. A group at Northwestern doing work roughly similar to the MIT/Harvard projects is also endeavoring to work out formulas for evaluating variable factors but it chooses to do this without the use of computers or even mathematical models. The group believes that while the computer has great capability, over-reliance upon it may cloud judgment. It points out that the most important and difficult part of a good analysis is not the computation; it is clear definition of the problem, the formulation of objectives, and the determination of which assumptions should be considered.

Technological forecasting

Technological forecasting is an extension and further tool of the systems approach. It is based on the premise that all technological advancement takes place in three steps—invention, innovation, and diffusion.

If one looks back into the history of inventions it is seen that their nature and occurrence are somewhat difficult to predict although it is clear that the type of invention is related to developing needs, and that the rate of occurrence is stimulated by periods of warfare or other crises.

The period of innovation, in the sense of technological forecasting, is the period required for the invention to be applied to basic uses or processes, as for example the period for the wheel to be applied to the cart, or gunpowder to the cannon. In early times the period required for innovation was relatively lengthy—often a matter of centuries. As the technological climate improved, the period required for the process of innovation was shortened until today in countries of advanced technology and communication the process may be completed in a few years, or even months.

Diffusion is the process by which innovations come into widespread use. Again the length of time required for this process has been reduced over the centuries.

Today, by studying the history of invention, innovation, and diffusion and assigning time values to the intervals, and by inventorying the present stage of each phase, it is possible to predict with a rather high degree of accuracy the technological probabilities for the next few decades at least. Such systematic anticipation of the direction, character, and timing of technical and economic progress assists in planning research, guiding programs, and carrying out long range planning, particularly in large scale national programs involving heavy capital investment—such as transportation.

It is clear that this emerging technique should be of interest to the Bureau of Public Roads, the Federal Highway Administration, and the Department of Transportation as well as state and local agencies. For as technology advances, the nature of highways and all modes of transportation and transit will change.

New horizons in urban freeway planning

Fifty years ago the automobile, destined to revolutionize the American way of life and of travel, was a novel plaything of the wealthy. The travel modes of 50 years from now are seeded for the most part in inventions yet to come.

Without doubt there will be radically changed types of vehicles and paths of movement. Perhaps congestion will force more transit and transportation into the air or water, or underground. But many technicians who should know predict that the revolution will come through improvement in the wheeled vehicle and in creative roadways and expressways with entirely new characteristics.

One may expect in the near future of automobile travel alone such features as:

Electronically controlled roadways on which vehicles may "lock in" to a guided system, to "cut out" again after having passed programmed terminal interchanges for individual takeover.

Individual auto units which may be fitted together for express transportation or for long distance movement within a larger transportation shell or wheeled carrier.

Long-distance movement of auto vehicles and passengers by jet tube or jet rail at flashing speeds.

Mandatory provision of force-field units on each vehicle to preclude collision.

Classification of highways to separate freight from other vehicular movement.

Eventual elimination of the bulk of freight vehicles from the highways by the construction of an intercity pneumatic tube freight transport system providing direct connection between all major air and sea ports and terminals.

Complete elimination of all through traffic routes within an urbanized complex.

New freeway cities in which roadways (and transit ways) will be completely integrated and centrally located garaging provided.

Apartment, commercial, or other structures and their related parking built to fit within the freeway corridor in which is reserved for highway purposes only the three-dimensional "air tunnels" required. Conversely, freeways may move through the city atop, through, or across commercial, institutional, light industrial, or residential structures, using air rights purchased or leased from the basic landowner.

The expanded use of public or private parking and recreation facilities under or alongside elevated highway structures or on decks or plazas above the roadway.

Incorporation into the city structure of publicly owned transportation-transit bands as paths to accommodate new systems of movement yet to be developed.

Self-financing of highway and perhaps other transportation-transit routes through excess land takings and leaseback of improved highway-related lands.

Urban freeways are but one element in the transportation inventory. There is today, as never before, a need for advancement in the means of moving people and goods. Certainly on the federal level nothing is at present more sorely needed than a masterful study aimed at the coordination of all forms of transport by water, air, and land. The planning of urban freeways can be carried forward only in this larger context.

In less than two decades through the use of computers, within the systems framework, we have learned to navigate ships, send rockets into space, and design weapons of incredible range and power. In basic highway engineering computers have cut a narrower swath. True, they have vastly simplified the computation of earthwork and of the dollar costs of alternate routes. But in the area of theory, and particularly in the attempted quantification of intangible values in highway and transportation planning, they have not yet been convincing.

While there may be arguments among the scientists concerning the limitations of computers in transportation studies, there is no dispute as to the value of the systems approach or its potential in highway planning. Certain aspects of systems analysis have been applied from time to time and to a greater or lesser degree in the solution of highway problems. It is now evident that the application of advanced techniques should be made general. The publication by the Bureau of Public Roads or the Department of Transportation of information on organization, methods, and procedures would be of great assistance as a guide to the state highway departments and the public agencies with which they work. A training program would also be of value.

Several questions arise. Who should call the systems approach into operation? Who should direct the team? Tradition, of course, would suggest that it be the highway engineer, and indeed much of the theoretical work in transportation planning is presently being conducted within the engineering departments of our universities. Others believe that the engineers are simply not equipped by training to make the extremely complicated decisions of tomorrow—decisions which hopefully will be integrating the highway and other transportation routes into the fiber of the urban community.

Some are convinced that the ultimate responsibility for the shape and form of the city must rest with the governing body of the city itself, and therefore the systems team should operate under some arm of the city government. Others point out that transportation problems transcend the city and even the county and conclude that they must therefore be the responsibility of the state working hand in hand with the local governments. Such thinking would lead to the formulation, within each state, of a total environmental planning body or commission, representing the most important state and local agencies and charged with the responsibility of reviewing and coordinating all physical planning within the state, specifically including highway projects.

On the federal level, it is proposed that, as a routine operation in the guidance, review, and long-range planning procedures of the Bureau of Public Roads, the Federal Highway Administration, and the Department of Transportation, the systems approach be employed to the limits of its present capacity. It is further proposed that these limits be extended and new techniques perfected through departmental research and substantial research grants to selected universities and to private research groups. For it is at the top that major responsibility and authority must lie. If our transportation systems are to guide as well as serve the growth of our neighborhoods, our cities, and our states, the impetus and direction must come from the Department of Transportation.

Bibliography

AASHO Publication List
American Association of State Highway Officials.
Washington, D.C., 1968

AMERICAN ASSOCIATION OF STATE HIGHWAY OFFICIALS
A Policy on Arterial Highways in Urban Areas.
Washington, D.C., 1957

APPLEYARD, DONALD, KEVIN LYNCH, AND JOHN R. MYER
The View from the Road.
M.I.T. Press, Cambridge, 1964

BACON, EDMUND N.
Design of Cities.
Viking Press, New York, 1967

BARNETT, JOSEPH
Urban Freeways and Center City Planning and Design.
Journal of the A.S.C.E. Urban Planning & Development Division, December 1966

BARNETT, JOSEPH
Rail Transit in the Median—Yes or No?
Civil Engineering, January 1963

BILL, MAX
Robert Maillart.
Erlenbach-Zurich, Verlag Fur Architektur, 1949

BUCHANAN, COLIN, AND OTHERS
Traffic in Towns, A Study of the Long Term Problems of Traffic in Urban Areas.
Great Britain, Ministry of Transport
H. M. Stationery Office, London, 1963

CHAPIN, F. STUART, JR.
Urban Land Use Planning.
University of Illinois Press, Urbana, Illinois, 1965

CROWE, SYLVIA
The Landscape of Roads.
The Architectural Press, London, 1960

CULLEN, GORDON
Townscape.
Reinhold, New York, 1961

GALLION, ARTHUR B., AND SIMON EISNER
The Urban Pattern.
Van Nostrand, Princeton, New Jersey, 1963

HALL, ARTHUR
A Methodology for Systems Engineering.
Van Nostrand, Princeton, New Jersey, 1962

HALPRIN, LAWRENCE
Cities.
Reinhold, New York, 1963

HALPRIN, LAWRENCE
Freeways.
Reinhold, New York, 1966

HERSHEY CONFERENCE, THE
Freeways in the Urban Setting.
Automotive Safety Foundation, Washington, D.C., 1962

HOLMES, E. H.
Looking 25 Years Ahead in Highway Development in the United States.
British Road Federation Monthly Bulletin, May 1965

INSTITUTE OF TRAFFIC ENGINEERS
System Considerations for Urban Freeways.
Washington, D.C., 1967

JACOBS, JANE
The Death and Life of Great American Cities.
Random House, New York, 1961

JELLICOE, G. A.
Motopia; A Study in Evolution of Urban Landscape.
Frederick A. Praeger, New York, 1961

LOUTZENHEISER, DONALD W.
New Concepts for Urban Freeway Interchanges.
Proceedings, American Society of Civil Engineers.
Journal of Highway Division, May 1962

LYNCH, KEVIN
The Image of the City.
The Technology Press and Harvard University Press,
Cambridge, Mass., 1960

MACKAYE, BENTON
The New Exploration: A Philosophy of Regional Planning.
University of Illinois Press, Urbana, Illinois, 1962

Massachusetts Institute of Technology Report No. 8
Project Metran. An Integrated, Evolutionary Transportation System for Urban Areas.
M.I.T. Press, Cambridge, Mass., 1966

MOCK, ELIZABETH B.
The Architecture of Bridges.
Museum of Modern Art, New York, 1949

MYER, JOHN R., JOHN F. KAIN, AND MARTIN WOHL
Technology and Urban Transportation.
Office of Science and Technology,
Executive Office of the President, Washington, 1962

MYER, JOHN R., AND OTHERS
The Urban Transportation Problem.
Harvard University Press, Cambridge, Mass., 1965

NATIONAL COMMITTEE ON URBAN TRANSPORTATION
Better Transportation for your City.
Public Administration Service, Chicago, 1958

New Highways: Challenge to the Metropolitan Region.
Technical Bulletin No. 31, Urban Land Institute,
Washington, D.C., 1958

OPPERMANN, LOGAN, AND TUCKER
Environmental Engineering and Metropolitan Planning.
Northwestern University Press, Evanston, Illinois, 1962

Oppermann, Paul
Metropolitan Area Approach to Comprehensive and Coordinated Transportation Planning.
Urban Transportation Planning, Bulletin No. 326
National Academy of Sciences, Highway Research Board, Washington, D.C., 1962

Pell, Claiborne
Megalopolis Unbound.
Frederick A. Praeger, New York and Washington, 1966

Proceedings of the White House Conference on Natural Beauty, Washington, D.C.
    May 24–25, 1965.
Government Printing Office, Washington, D.C. 1965

Rapuano, Michael, P. P. Pirone, and Brooks E. Wigginton
Open Space in Urban Design.
Cleveland Development Foundation and the Junior League of Cleveland, Inc.
Spiral Press, New York, 1964

Ritter, Paul
Planning for Man and Motor.
Macmillan, New York, 1964

Sagamore Conference on Highways and Urban Development, Syracuse University, 1958
Guidelines for Action.
Joint Committee on Highways of the American Municipal Association and the
    American Association of State Highway Officials, Washington, D.C.

Simonds, John O.
Landscape Architecture, the Shaping of Man's Natural Environment.
McGraw-Hill, New York, 1961

Smith, Wilbur and Associates
Future Highways and Urban Growth.
Automobile Manufacturers Association
New Haven, Conn., 1961

Snow, Brewster
The Highway and the Landscape.
Rutgers University Press, New Brunswick, N.J., 1959

Spreiregen, Paul D.
Urban Design: The Architecture of Towns and Cities.
McGraw-Hill, New York, 1965

Transportation and Parking for Tomorrow's Cities.
Automobile Manufacturers Association
New Haven, Conn., 1966

TUNNARD, CHRISTOPHER, AND BORIS PUSHKAREV
Man-Made America: Chaos or Control?
Yale University Press, New Haven and London, 1963

Twentieth Century Engineering.
Museum of Modern Art, New York, 1964

U.S. BUREAU OF PUBLIC ROADS
Highways and Human Values.
U.S. Government Printing Office, Washington, D.C., 1967

UNITED STATES DEPARTMENT OF COMMERCE
Freeways to Urban Development.
U.S. Government Printing Office, Washington, D.C., 1966

UNITED STATES DEPARTMENT OF COMMERCE
*Highway Transportation Criteria in Zoning law and Police Power and Planning
    Controls of Arterial Streets.*
U.S. Bureau of Public Roads, Washington, D.C., 1960

WATSON, WILBUR J.
Bridge Architecture.
Helburn Press, New York, 1927

What Freeways Mean to Your City.
Automotive Safety Foundation
Washington, D.C., 1964

WHYTE, WILLIAM H. Jr.
Securing Open Space for Urban America; Conservation Easements.
Urban Land Institute, Technical Bulletin No. 36
Washington, D.C., 1959

WILLIAMSBURG CONFERENCE. THE SECOND NATIONAL CONFERENCE ON HIGHWAYS AND
    URBAN DEVELOPMENT, WILLIAMSBURG, VIRGINIA, 1965
Highways and Urban Development.
American Association of State Highway Officials, National Association of Counties, and
    National League of Cities

WOHL, MARTIN, AND BRIAN V. MARTIN
Traffic System Analysis.
McGraw-Hill, New York, 1967

Glossary

ACQUISITION OR TAKING The process of obtaining right-of-way.

ARTERIAL HIGHWAY A highway used primarily for through traffic, usually on a continuous route.

AUXILIARY LANE The portion of the roadway adjoining the traveled way for parking, speed change, or for other purposes supplementary to through traffic movement.

AVERAGE DAILY TRAFFIC The average 24 hour volume, being the total volume during a stated period divided by the number of days in that period. Unless otherwise stated, the period is a year. The term is commonly abbreviated as ADT.

BELT HIGHWAY An arterial highway for carrying traffic partially or entirely around an urban area or portion thereof. (Also called "circumferential highway").

BUS A motor vehicle designed for the transportation of more than 10 persons.

CENTRAL BUSINESS DISTRICT That center or core within the embracing region in which is concentrated the most intensive commercial activity.

CENTRAL CITY The urbanized area surrounding and including the central business district. A large and densely populated center of economic, social, and political activity.

COMMUNITY A common habitat or the totality of all persons living in the same area, with limits as large as the local economic and social interdependence of the people. It is the smallest local group which may comprise a complete society. It is usually served by its own high school, churches, shopping center, and other communal facilities.

COMPUTER PROGRAMMING The devising of a series of operations to be performed by a computer.

CONDEMNATION The process by which property is acquired for highway purposes through legal proceedings under power of eminent domain.

CONTROL OF ACCESS The condition where the right of owners or occupants of abutting land or other persons to access, light, air, or view in connection with a highway is fully or partially controlled by public authority.

CUL-DE-SAC STREET A local street open at one end only and with special provision for turning around.

DEAD-END STREET A local street open at one end only without special provision for turning around.

DESIGN SPEED   A speed determined for design and correlation of the physical features of a highway that influence vehicle operation. It is the maximum safe speed that can be maintained over a specified section of highway when conditions are favorable.

DIVIDED HIGHWAY   A highway with separated roadways for traffic in opposite directions.

EASEMENT   A right acquired by public authority to use or control property for a designated highway purpose.

EMINENT DOMAIN   The power to take property for public use with just compensation.

EXPRESSWAY   A divided arterial highway for through traffic with full or partial control of access. In this report, full control of access is implied, and the term is used interchangeably with the word "freeway."

FEEDBACK   The return to the input of a part of the output of a machine, system, or process that contains information on discrepancies between intended and actual performance and leads to a self-correction of the system.

FREEWAY   An expressway with full control of access.

FRONTAGE STREET OR FRONTAGE ROAD   A local street or road auxiliary to and located on the side of an arterial highway for service to abutting property and adjacent areas.

GRADE SEPARATION A crossing of two highways, or a highway and a railroad, at different levels.

HIGHEST AND BEST USE   The most productive use, reasonable but not speculative or conjectural, to which property may be put in the near future.

HIGHWAY OR STREET   A general term denoting a public way for purposes of vehicular travel, including the entire area within the right-of-way.

HUMAN FACTORS   The physiological and psychological capacities of man.

INPUT   Information fed into a computer.

INTERCHANGE   A grade-separated intersection with one or more turning roadways for travel between intersection legs.

INTERSECTION   The general area where two or more highways join or cross, within which are included the roadway and roadside facilities for traffic movements in that area.

ISLAND   A defined area between traffic lanes for control of vehicle movements or for pedestrian refuge. Within an intersection a median or an outer separation is considered an island.

LOCAL STREET   A street used primarily for access to residential, business, or other abutting property.

MAJOR STREET OR MAJOR HIGHWAY   An arterial highway with intersections at grade and direct access to abutting property, and on which geometric design and traffic control measures are used to expedite the safe movement of through traffic.

MATHEMATICAL MODEL   (1) A mathematical representation of an object, event, process, or concept. (2) A series of quantitative terms that describe the structure or behavior of real systems.

MAXIMIZE   To increase to the highest possible degree.

MEDIAN   The portion of a divided highway separating the traveled ways for traffic in opposite directions.

MEDIAN LANE   A speed-change lane within the median to accommodate left-turning vehicles.

MINIMIZE   To reduce to the smallest possible degree.

MODEL   A representation of an object, event, process, or concept that is used for prediction and control. By manipulating the model, the effects of changing one or more aspects of the entity represented can be determined.

NEIGHBORHOOD   A primary informal group consisting of all persons who live in local proximity. Often considered to be the locality served by an elementary school or neighborhood convenience shopping center. Neighborhoods form the more or less cohesive cells of a larger community.

OPERATIONS RESEARCH   The application of analytical methods to the problems of organizational control by interdisciplinary teams interested in the performance of whole systems. The term is commonly abbreviated as "OR."

OUTER SEPARATION   The portion of an arterial highway between the traveled ways of a roadway for through traffic and a frontage street or road.

OUTPUT   Information produced by a computer.

OVERPASS   A grade separation where the subject highway passes over an intersecting highway or railroad.

PARAMETER   (1) Mathematical term for a symbolic quantity that may be associated with some measurable quantity in the real world (e.g., length). (2) Any part of a system that can be deliberately changed.

PARKING LANE   An auxiliary lane primarily for the parking of vehicles.

PARKWAY   An arterial highway for non-commercial traffic, with full or partial control of access, usually located within a park or a ribbon of parklike developments.

PASSENGER CAR   A motor vehicle designed for the transportation of not more than 10 persons.

PRINCIPLE   A fundamental and truthful guide derived from observation.

QUANTIFIABLE FACTORS   Those factors in the consideration of a process or problem, such as in urban or freeway planning and design, for which numerical or dollar values may be determined and assigned.

RADIAL HIGHWAY   An arterial highway leading to or from an urban center.

ROADSIDE   A general term denoting the area adjoining the outer edge of the roadway. Extensive areas between the roadways of a divided highway may also be considered roadside.

ROADSIDE CONTROL   The public regulation of the roadside to improve highway safety, expedite the free flow of traffic, safeguard present and future highway investment, conserve abutting property values, or preserve the attractiveness of the landscape.

ROADSIDE ZONING   The application of zoning for roadside control.

ROADWAY   The portion of a highway, including shoulders, for vehicular use. A divided highway has two or more roadways.

SHOULDER   The portion of the roadway contiguous with the traveled way for accommodation of stopped vehicles, for emergency use, and for lateral support of base and surface courses.

SPEED-CHANGE LANE   An auxiliary lane, including tapered areas, primarily for the acceleration or deceleration of vehicles entering or leaving the through traffic lanes.

STANDARD   A prescribed criterion of acceptable, usually minimum-dimension, quality or performance.

SYSTEM   (1) A complex unity formed of many diverse parts. (2) An aggregation of objects jointed in regular interaction or interdependence. (3) Any set of objects or events with relationships between them or their attributes.

SYSTEMS ANALYSIS   (1) A term often used almost synonymously with "operations research" to describe a research or decision-making process by which alternative approaches to overall design, or to a problem, are considered in order to arrive at a system that provides optimum performance with respect to established criteria. (2) Sometimes described as a phase of systems studies following systems synthesis in which consequences are deduced from alternative systems on costs, performance, etc.

SYSTEMS APPROACH   (1) Loosely, looking at the overall situation rather than the narrow implications of the task at hand; particularly, looking for inter-relationships between the task at hand and other functions which relate to it. (2) The methods used by systems analysis and "operations research" men in solving problems.

SYSTEMS CONCEPTS   A term referring to the whole body of ideas and techniques of systems analysis and "operations research."

SYSTEMS ENGINEERING   (1) A term often used as a general term synonymous with systems analysis and "operations research." (2) More specifically, the implementation of the system decisions through the design and supervision of the components and subsystems.

TRAFFIC CONTROL DEVICE   Any sign, signal, marking or installation placed or erected under public authority, for the purpose of regulating, warning, or guiding traffic.

TRAFFIC LANE   The portion of the traveled way for the movement of a single line of vehicles.

TRAVELED WAY   The portion of the roadway for the movement of vehicles, exclusive of shoulders and auxiliary lanes.

UNDERPASS   A grade separation where the subject highway passes over an intersecting highway or railroad.

VOLUME   The number of vehicles passing a given point during a specified period of time.

ZONING   The division of a city or region into districts and the application of different regulations in each district to govern the use of the land. Implied is the public control of the use of property in the interest of the public at large.

Acknowledgments

John O. Simonds   EDITOR

Walter McQuade   EDITORIAL CONSULTATION AND ASSIGNMENT OF PHOTOGRAPHY

Jan V. White   BOOK DESIGN

Franklin Pugh   PUBLICATION COORDINATOR

ILLUSTRATIONS:

Sixty of the drawings in this report were reproduced from original sketch diagrams by the editor. Most of the others were adapted from sketches by the other Urban Advisors.

   Delineation by Robert Bennett, Donald Vogan, Philip Winslow and Paul Wolfe.

Republished illustrations include:

    pages 82-83:   design by Skidmore, Owings and Merrill for Market Street East; courtesy of the Philadelphia City Planning Commission and the Redevelopment Authority of the City of Philadelphia.

    page 84:   drawing by Mark de Nalovy Rozvadovski; courtesy of McMillan, Griffis and Mileto, Architects.

             from drawing of Princes Street by-pass scheme, Edinburgh, Scotland, by Sir Patrick Abercrombie and Derek Plumstead.

PHOTOGRAPHS:

U. S. GOVERNMENT PRINTING OFFICE : 1968 O - 296-930